COLOR T~~~~
for Cl~~~~

M000104739

A Practical Guide for Anyone Sharing Moments with Children

MARYANNE E. HOFFMAN
America's Leading Child Color Therapist

★ STAR VISIONS ★

★ ★ A Rainbow of Gratitude ★ ★

The author expresses a special rainbow of appreciation and thanks to Joyce A. Minor for her valuable assistance and time, Melinda Ule-Grohol for her special contributions and Douglas Cerroni for his gracious consideration. Rainbow Blessings to you!

Color Therapy For Children
Copyright © 1998 by Maryanne E. Hoffman

Author photo by John Barr, *USA Today*
Cover and interior illustrations by Maryanne E. Hoffman
Copyright © 1984, *Mystical Messages*; Star Gazers, greeting card line.
Copyright © 1985, *Mystical Messages*; Color Card, greeting card line.
Copyright © 1998, Rainbow Play, Personality Color Assessment

Library of Congress Cataloging-in-Publication Data

Hoffman, Maryanne E.
    Color therapy for children

    1. Color therapy. 2. Color therapy - Therapeutic use.
3. Child development. 4. Art therapy.   I. Title

ISBN 0-943299-92-6

First edition published, December, 1998

Made in the U. S. A.
Printed on Recycled Paper using soy-based inks

About The Author

MARYANNE E. HOFFMAN, MA, CCT

A pioneer in the field of color therapy. Ms. Hoffman has conducted extensive research on color for over fifteen years and is a certified *color therapist*. Now for the first time in this book, she introduces the *Rainbow Play©* Personality Color Assessment for children. Through the uses of color and inventive activities, Ms. Hoffman illustrates the role of color in a child's world for well-being, healing, activity and self-discovery.

Ms. Hoffman, is recognized for her innovative methodology and research in the fields of art and color therapy, *en lieu* of a doctoral degree from Ohio State University. She obtained a Master's degree from Ohio University and a B.F.A. degree from the Ohio State University. She studied medical technology at Youngstown State University and worked as a medical technician specialized in microbiology in hospitals for over 15 years. She has taught at various institutions in Ohio and Pennsylvania including Ohio State University, Ohio University, the Cleveland Museum of Art and the Butler Institute of American Art. She instructs color therapy at Lakeland Community College in Cleveland, Ohio.

In her work on color, Ms. Hoffman has founded the Rainbow Rising Institute of American Color Therapy which provides Color Therapy and Color Specialty certification through in-house correspondence courses. She is founder and president of the American Color Therapy Association.

In addition to this book, Ms. Hoffman has also written and illustrated three others; *THE RAINBOW IN YOUR LIFE, PERSONAL DREAM DIARY,* and *THE GODDESS GUIDE.* Ms. Hoffman's expertise and work in the field of color and related areas has generated a number of guest appearances on TV and radio programs across the United States and Canada.

To learn more about color, color therapy and the Rainbow Rising Institute of American Color Therapy, visit Ms. Hoffman's web site at **RAINBOWRISING.COM**.

Melinda Ule-Grohol

Introduction

In this book about color therapy you will discover many new ways of using colors of the rainbow for children. Although color therapy is an aged old discipline, its use for child development, personality assessment and understanding of the whole child is innovative.

In modern times the field of color has held importance in commercial advertising and the industrial setting. This book gives extensive information on color for children that is specifically directed to the needs of the individual, who does not have knowledge in color therapy.

It is a scientific fact we perceive knowledge through electromagnetic radiation known as light. Light visible and invisible is an electric field of energy comprised of long and short waves, which are indicated by their specific colors creating the rainbow.

Color is a sensation in our consciousness. We are able to perceive color through the retina of our eyes as light passes through them. The blind also sense the vibration of color without seeing color. When we look at an object, the sky, or a person we absorb a series of multiple wavelengths of light that reflect color from that object.

This book focuses on children as they express themselves through the spectrum of the rainbow. In my research I continue to discover that children's sensitivity to color is reflected in their developmental stage and their changing personality. Whether a child is blind or color blind certain colors are recognized and preferred for cognitive development. Newborns through preschool age respond to the neutrals black and white and later red; preschoolers to red, blue and yellow and elmenatry school children orange, green and violet. As children develop their color preferences become a selection from the rainbow. Color reveals children's personality, physical condition, emotional, mental and spiritual well-being. This book is a practical reference for every area of a child's world.

The artwork preceding each section and on the back cover of the book illustrates the meaning of the color it represents.

These circular paintings were created to facilitate personal centering and for **Rainbow Play**© Personality Color Assessment.

In this practical reference of the rainbow you will find suggestions for using color as a significant part of children's everyday world from color preferences for sports and activities to color for encouraging positive behavior. Explore the ways color affects a child's ability to learn and discover colors for physical, mental and spiritual well-being. Enjoy guiding children through a rainbow journey of personal discovery with *Color Therapy For Children*.

Maryanne E. Hoffman, October, 1998

Preface

Color Therapy For Children was envisioned through requests from readers, who found the information and color exercises in my book *The Rainbow In Your Life* helpful in their lives. This book addresses the rainbow needs of toddlers through preteens and is designed for anyone who shares moments with children and has an interest in their welfare and development. However, parental figures and professionals working with children will find the information very enlightening.

Through my love for and experiences with children as a color and art educator, I felt the need to explore simple ways others can help enhance a child's life through the use of color.Color is powerful in a simple and gentle way. The direct results of color influences are non-threatening which is an ideal vehicle to improve the lives of children.

The color therapy applications in this book do not require you to be an expert. They are tailored for safe and easy use for anyone. Explore and experiment with color suggestions for behavior modification, learning, environment and the total well-being for the children's empowerment.

You may find the section entitled **Fun with Auras** quite exciting both for you and the children. For over fifteen yeas I have researched the phenomenon of auras and have successfully instructed lecture audiences with my methods on how to read their aura. You will be able to not only see children's auras, but also your own. There has been much scientific data to substantiate the evidence of the aura and the meaning of their colors. Enjoy exploring auras.

The information in this book is the creative result of my professional and personal experiences with color. This book represents my rainbow of love for the hope to positively empower the children of today down through the generations for tomorrow. My visionary rainbow and I invite you to explore *Color Therapy For Children.*

MARYANNE E. HOFFMAN, October, 1998

Contents

EXPLORING A RAINBOW JOURNEY

MAGENTA SPECTRUM

Magenta is the essence of creativity, originality and individuality. It is the creative force of the imagination. Its magical effect enlivens the fantasy world within you and makes you special.

This simple and fun journey into children's worlds of color reveals much about how children feel on a daily basis and how children use their personal power.

Get to know children better through the coloring of their personal world. Most of children's color choices reflect the personality traits and emotions in that moment. Because children are developing, growing and constantly changing color choices may vary daily, weekly or monthly. Pay close attention to colors that are repeated over a certain amount of time. This may indicate a core personality trait or a physical or emotional condition that needs attention.

This is not a psychological test - it is a personal discovery journey, designed to create awareness of children's unique qualities as individuals and to give greater understanding of their personal space.

STEP ONE

CREATING THE CHILDREN'S OWN SPECIAL RAINBOW

For the best results give step one and step two on the same day. It is important to remember not to influence the children's choice of color in any way. Be neutral as possible when asking the questions. Remember for young children creating is a natural process. Give children the seven colors of the rainbow plus gray, black, brown and white to create a rainbow with any materials; crayons, pastels, paint or colored pencil. Younger children love to paint. Ask the children to make their own special imaginary rainbow. Remind the children that this is not a test. Ask them to paint a rainbow with their favorite color on top to their least favorite on the bottom. It is best to explain the sequence for each specific section. Example: Paint your favorite color on top, now your next favorite color below the top one, now your next favorite, etc. Continue the use of all the colors by process of elimination. The last arch should be their least favorite color. Do not rush the children. This process needs to be done at the their own pace.

STEP TWO

Have the children respond spontaneously to the series of

questions below. Remember to suggest using their imagination. The color key to questions 1, 2, 7, and 8 is at the end of this chapter on page 13.

1. Which do you enjoy the best: sunrise, high noon, sunset?
2. What is your favorite season: winter, spring, summer, fall?
3. Which color do you like best: red, blue, yellow?
4. Which color do you like best: orange, purple, green?
5. Which color do you like best: black, gray, white?
6. What two combined colors do you like best?
7. Which shape is most appealing to you?

circle ◯	square ☐	triangle △
oval ◯	hexagon ⬡	rectangle ▭
crescent ☽		

8. Which line is most appealing to you?

horizontal ▬	vertical ❘	diagonal ╱
curved ∿	jagged ⋏	wavy ∿
check mark ✓		

THE RAINBOW JOURNEY'S END

At the completion of the rainbow journey note the three dominant color choices for step one and two combined.

WARM PERSONALITY

If the three colors fall into two or three variations of the following colors: red, orange and yellow the child is an extroverted personality, actively seeking change, assertive in behavior and enjoys attention and a leadership position among peers. Others may admire and look up to the child's strong convictions and ambitious nature. If the child is in the warm category, she/he is an outward person needing an environment that will adapt to all her/his activities.

COOL PERSONALITY

If the child chooses two or more of the following variations: blue, green, purple/violet and indigo these are the cool colors, more passive in nature and people-oriented.The child may consider other's opinions and is willing to compromise and please them.The child likes peace and quiet, and often needs to retreat from the outside world. Peers may see the child as a good follower or quiet leader. The child is an inward person who needs an environment not so stimulating but more soothing and peaceful where she/he can feel secure and nurtured.

NEUTRAL PERSONALITY

If the neutrals, white, gray, brown and black dominate in two or three selections, the child is in an interim phase in her/his life situation and may be on the periphery of great change.

If the child selects a mix of warm and/or cool and a neutral the child desires an environment filled with many activities and choices to avoid boredom. The child is open to numerous changes in activities as well as moods.

This is a simple assessment of a child's unique color scheme as it applies to her/his personal journey. In further chapters each color will be explored more specifically. *You have just colored the surface!*

Color Interpretation For Exploring A Rainbow Journey

1. Sunrise/Blue - High Noon/Yellow - Sunset/Red.

2. Winter/Indigo - Spring/Green - Summer/Orange - Fall/Violet.

7. Circle/Blue - Square/Red - Triangle/Yellow - Oval/Violet
   Rectangle/Orange - Hexagon/Green -Crescent/Indigo.

8. Horizontal/Blue - Vertical/Red - Curved/Violet - Wavy/Indigo
   Diagonal/Orange - Jagged/Yellow - Check Mark/Green.

RAINBOW PLAY

SPECTRUM IN RED

Red is the color of pure energy, the flame of love, passion, and courage.It is the vibrant force of life itself! Its dynamic effect brings you intense experiences and fullness of daily living.

CHILDREN'S COLOR PERSONALITY

INSTRUCTIONS FOR RAINBOW PLAY©

The Color Mandalas on the back of the book cover were specifically designed for each color of the rainbow and its special meaning. Use the back cover for Rainbow Play©. It is important to consider that the selection of colors can change daily. Repetitive color patterns or the same color choices that occur in the same position for a period of weeks or months at a time may indicate that a particular developmental stage is in progress or a strong personality trait is expressed. This is not a test, so make this an enjoyable experience for the child.

1. Construct two columns numbered 1 through 7.

2. Instruct the child to scan the seven color mandalas for just a minute and decide what colors she/he likes best. Inform the child not to relate the colors to any object, holiday or thing.

3. Instruct the child to select the colors in order of preference (from the most liked to the least favorite). Make certain that the child selects the colors quickly without much analysis. Once the child selects the first favorite color cover the selection with a white piece of paper. Write down the color selected as number one.

4. Have the child scan the other colors and choose the next favorite color from the remaining selection. After each color chosen cover the mandala with a white piece of paper. Repeat number 4 until all the colors have been selected. Write down the color selections in order of preference.

5. Begin at the second column and repeat the process over again. Turn the book upside down, so that the colors are in different positions. Repeat numbers 2 to 4. Do not expect the child to repeat the exact same selections. Have the child choose the colors as if she/he were seeing them for the first time.

6. Record the color selections in the second column.

INTRODUCTORY INTERPRETATIONS

1. Notice if the color selections in both columns are identical or varied. Usually the second selection is more accurate then the first. Use the second column for the interpretation of Rainbow Play©. If the child's selections in both columns are different that implies the child is flexible and open for changes and learning. If both columns are identical, this indicates the child is more rigid or stubborn in her/his current situation.

2. From the second column, group the seven colors in pairs. Circle the selections in sequential pairs of two. Group all the selection of colors next to one another. Example:

1. red 2. orange 3. blue 4. green 5. violet 6. yellow 7. indigo

3. Example: Group 1 and 2 together (1. red and 2. orange). Then group 2 and 3 together (2. orange and 3. blue). Continue to group all the colors next to each other.

4. Turn to the section on **Interpretations to Color Combinations** (p.17) in this chapter for the meaning of the color pairs. Example: 3. blue and 4. green - (p. 20) **Blue with Green** - You project a peaceful, stress-free and responsible nature. You are sensitive to the feelings of others and are observant with an eye for detail.

5. The pairs 1 - 2 and 2 - 3 indicate the desired personality of the child. Pairs number 3 - 4 and 4 - 5 indicate the actual personality and behavior traits of the child. Pairs 5 - 6 and 6 - 7 are traits the child has least developed.

6. Refer to the section in this chapter on **Color Choices For First And Last Place** (p.15) to interpret the first selection and the last selection. The first selection number 1. indicates what the child is developing and the last position number 7. indicates what the child is rejecting or needs to develop. Example: Red as number 1 indicates a leader and an extroverted personality. Indigo as number 7 demonstrates that the child has a need for loyalty, trust, and greater understanding.

COLOR CHOICES FOR FIRST AND LAST PLACE

The color in the first and second positions indicate the personality traits children desire and are currently developing. The last two selections in sixth and seventh positions reflect the personality trait children reject and may need to develop.

The selection of the warm colors red, orange or yellow in the first and second positions indicates an outgoing and extroverted personality. The rejection of these colors in the sixth and seventh position reflects a need to integrate these qualities into the personality. The selection of the cool colors green, blue, indigo, or violet in the first and second positions, indicates a passive personality with more introverted traits. The rejection of these colors in the sixth and seventh position reveals a need to integrate these traits into the personality. The mixture of both a warm and cool color in either position gives a greater balance to the personality.

RED

Children favoring red demonstrate an aggressive manner, assertive attitude and a dynamic out-going personality. Personal survival, self-direction, independence and pleasurable satisfaction are paramount in their daily routine. Red is popular with the extrovert, and the dynamically energized personality. They are interested and intensely involved in physical activities, adventure, fun and games. Impulsively traveling on the spur of the moment, excitement is their motto. They are charged with great endurance and are highly spirited in all their projects and activities.

ORANGE

Children favoring orange indicate that they have high aspirations and love to partake in group activities. They are mannered, considerate and have a cheerful disposition, which makes them popular in social situations. They achieve their goals best with support from others. They desire success and most likely will achieve it through popularity and a sense of humor. Their inventive abilities and self assurance marks them as creative leaders. Fun loving and silly, they like to play harmless tricks on peers. They often make decisions through logical deduction and intellectualization. Self-control is essential for their emotional well-being.

YELLOW

Children favoring yellow demonstrate a whirlwind of energy when engaged in projects and pursuit of important goals for their future. They are capable of doing well in a variety of interests and accomplishing their numerous goals simultaneously. They are likened to the skillful artist creating form from the formless, inventing something new and progressive in their world. They have a need for change and want to modify outworn habits and stagnant circumstances in the hope of expecting greater happiness in a new situation. Their minds tend to be scientific and they enjoy intellectual challenges and debate. Their abundant vitality, tenacity and intense commitment to their projects mark them as unusual leaders of progressive thinking, reform and a new tomorrow.

GREEN

Children favoring green are impressive and commanding in a leadership position among peers. They are helpful, tenacious, and persevering with important relationships and responsibilities. Adaptable and flexible in nature, they try to maintain self-control and a friendly disposition in most situations. They are proud of their accomplishments and require recognition for them. Their inner urge is to remain close to nature and participate in the dance of life and its celebration, through experiencing well-being in mind, body and spirit.

BLUE

Children favoring blue are devoted and loyal to their friends, pets and family. Their spiritual and/or religious beliefs and moral principles are very important to them. They prefer friends who have similar family background and interest. They need relationships for emotional security and inner harmony. They tend to be peaceful and reflective with a nature requiring an orderly existence. They are somewhat introverted and introspective. Their outstanding traits are sincerity, diplomacy and responsibility. They function best with the support and nurturing from someone they admire. Their ultimate goal is to live in a world of peace, harmony and brotherly love.

INDIGO

Favoring indigo reveals the children's inner need to sustain an idealized sense of harmony with themselves and in their important personal relationships. They are discriminating in important situations and possess a very logical mind with great mental abilities. Their ability to be unselfish and enthusiastic toward the development and attainments of others marks them as respected and admired leaders among their peers. Their affectionate and self-sacrificing nature needs to share with a warm, bonded relationship in an atmosphere of sensitivity, love, peace and beauty. They will not compromise their beliefs, ethics or principles, but they will influence others to their side through loving understanding and unselfish efforts. Harmony and peacemaking with everyone is their ultimate goal.

VIOLET

Children favoring violet demonstrate a sense of nobility, magical charm and a tremendous imagination. They are the true individualists, the seekers of philosophy and truth. They intensely follow their intuition over logical thinking. Desiring a fantasy or mystical relationship, their creative imagination is seemingly real. All the arts appeal to them and they have the energy required to participate in the arts enthusiastically and with much dedication. Possessing many unique qualities, they are the true romanticist and idealist who try to develop perfection in all their affairs. Their affectionate nature endears them to everyone. They are the royal kings or queens in their world of life's treasures. They are the jewels!

INTERPRETATIONS OF COLOR COMBINATIONS

RED

Red/Orange - indicates an overly expressive and reactive nature. General manifestations include hyperactivity, spontaneity and the concentration of intense energy on one particular experience with the ability to change the focus at a sudden notice.

17

Red/Yellow - reveals a desire to experience life to the fullest. General manifestations include: enthusiasm and receptivity to new experiences and a self-confident and optimistic nature with an intense drive toward achievement of goals. The winner or overachiever.

Red/Green - indicates a need to be assertive and exercise great will-power toward pursuing goals. A domineering and self-assured personality.

Red/Blue - indicates a desire for a life of rich experiences and intense involvement. A need for a close relationship with emotional bonding.

Red/Indigo - indicates a desire to participate in special interests groups as a dynamic and courageous leader. A need to express unique qualities and individuality among peers and a desire for unity among diversity.

Red/Violet - reveals a magical personality with charm and effervescence, very theatrical in nature, and the ability to have a magnetic hold with considerable influence on others.

ORANGE

Orange/Red - reveals a demanding nature with the desire to be the center of attention. A need to be important and stand out among peers.

Orange/Yellow - indicates a need for positive acceptance and popularity, a desire to make new friends and reaching out for attention and friendly interaction with others.

Orange/Green - reveals a warm, yet controlled personality and a desire to be friends with everyone. The class clown and/or humorous nature.

Orange/Blue - indicates a wild and gregarious personality with a great sense of humor. A desire to be popular.

Orange/Indigo - indicates a need for support and emotional bonding with family members. General manifestations include an amicable image and loyalty toward a cause or a special group.

18

Orange /Violet - reveals a need for social acceptance and to express their true feelings, originality in unique ways and/or a harmless rebel. The laugh of the party or clown.

YELLOW

Yellow/Red - reveals the desire to achieve their hopes and dreams and to count in their world. A restless urge to spread themselves too thin over too many activities to feel greater self-esteem. The overachiever.

Yellow/Orange - general manifestations are: a warm and outgoing nature, talkative and direct and to the point. They project self-confidence and have smart planning and organizational skills.

Yellow/Green - indicates sharp awareness and keen observation for opportunities that offer individual freedom and self-growth. A strong urge to achieve recognition and self-actualization. The ability to extend greater understanding between themselves and others.

Yellow/Blue - reveals a desire for contentment and harmony through relationships that are affectionate and promote good will. General manifestations are: a positive, self-accepting image and openness to new avenues and ideas that are successful and exciting. A need for mutual understanding and warmth from others.

Yellow/Indigo - indicates a need to pursue and lead others into new endeavors that provide progressive change. General characteristics are: positive assurance, mature outlook on life and a cheerful attitude toward others.

Yellow/Violet - indicates a need to express their overly active imagination and vivid fantasies through exciting pursuits and the theatrical arts. They seek admiration for a charming and magical personality. They have a bent for metaphysics and are visionary about their future.

GREEN

Green/Red - indicates a need to be independent and self-oriented toward success. They have strength and endurance to overcome all obstacles and to make proper decisions pursuing their objectives. They can single-handedly accomplish their tasks.

Green/Orange - reveals a desire for a friendly and warm relationship that allows them to exercise their free-will. A mature adventurous and gregarious spirit.

Green/Yellow - reveals a need for popularity and admiration for their impressive ambitions. A harmonious attitude in their attempt to bridge the gap between themselves and others.

Green/Blue - indicates tremendous sensitivity and the need to express their individuality for acknowledgment. A desire to make a favorable impression and receive proper recognition for their abilities and talents.

Green/Indigo - reveals a need to exercise their will-power and be heard in family matters and groups. A cool, calm disposition with quiet self-assurance.

Green/Violet - original in their personal style they need to be noticed as a special personality. They desire special recognition and influence through having control over situations.

BLUE

Blue/Red - indicates a desire for a harmonious, affectionate and compatible relationship. A loving, trusting and self-sacrificing nature.

Blue/Orange - indicates a kindly disposition and an ability to compromise with others for mutual goals. They are trustworthy and sincere in friendship. They desire a mutually caring and sharing equal relationship.

Blue/Yellow - indicates they project emotional enthusiasm. They are adaptable to another's needs with mutual understanding and consideration. They desire happiness and fulfillment through close relationship.

Blue/Green - indicates a pleasant personality. They project a peaceful, stress-free and responsible nature. They are sensitive to the feelings of others and are observant with an eye for detail.

Blue/Indigo - indicates a need to experience rest and tranquillity. A complacent and compromising nature.

Blue/Violet - indicates a need to express tenderness and emotional sensitivity in personal relationships and a desire for a deeply bonded relationship with a parent/parental figure. They are very responsive to beauty and affection.

INDIGO

Indigo/Red - reveals a trustworthy and fair disposition. They are enterprising with group or family goals.

Indigo/Orange - reveals a need to be included in all family or school activities. A reserved nature with an inner urge to befriend everyone.

Indigo/Yellow - indicates a desire to explore futuristic ideas and alternative group activities. They project an intuitive, witty and philosophical nature.

Indigo/Green - indicates a need to preserve family traditions. They project a well-rounded and considerate nature with a serious approach to important relationships.

Indigo/Blue - reveals a desire to blend in with all groups and to have a utopian attitude about life. They project a very trustworthy and loyal nature toward others.

Indigo/Violet - indicates a great need to live their spiritual beliefs and to express their creativity. They project a universal image, unbiased with total love for all humanity.

VIOLET

Violet/Red - indicates a desire for a relationship that is magical. They project a dynamic and charming personality.

Violet/Orange - reveals a need to express their creative and clever ideas in group situations. They project a wild sense of humor and like to play jokes on others.

Violet/Yellow - indicates a need for new and exciting experiences, an expressive charm and a popular personality. They
have a rich imagination and enjoy fantasizing.

Violet/Green - indicates a need to express their positive
traits to make a favorable impression on others, to gain
special recognition and considerable influence. They are
original and very sensitive to others' reactions to them.

Violet/Blue - indicates a desire for an idealized family
relationship with empathy, harmony, deep affection and
gentleness. They are responsive to esthetics and beauty.

Violet/Indigo - indicates a desire to express their creative
imagination and/or psychic ability and intuition. They project
a noble image, sincerity and unique individualism.

PERSONALITY PALETTE

FRIENDSHIP
SINCERITY
MYSTERY
ENTHUSIASM
NATURE
FREEDOM
KINDNESS

SPECTRUM IN ORANGE

Orange is the color of the luminous setting sun. It is life's creative force- the pulse of nature vibrating through the earth. It symbolizes the harvest- the abundant fruits of the earth. The mystery of time is its essence. Use orange in your daily life for positive social interaction.

The most effective colors to enhance children's needs and to promote their personal power are the seven colors of the rainbow. Wearing these colors in any color type combined with one another and/or the neutrals brown, gray, black and white convey unconscious messages to others around them.

Color can be used effectively for any personal, educational, social, or formal situation. Color is the power of the unspoken word and sends out signals loud and clear. When considering the color combinations review the section entitled **Interpretations of Color Combinations** under **Rainbow Play** © . Consider the major color as the dominant color and the other color as the accent color such as for a child's apparel. Example: orange with yellow. Orange is the major color and yellow is the accent color. An orange outfit with yellow informs others that the child has a strong desire for positive acceptance and friendly interaction with playmates. The child evokes a likable personality and is open to forming new friends. This color combination is especially helpful when a child is in a situation of meeting or interacting with new people. For example the first day of school. This color combination is not only warm and friendly but also fun and gregarious. It is excellent for a shy or withdrawn child.

The colors children wear project a particular image to others. They can enhance their personality and affect how they relate to others and how others respond to them. A color in its purest hue has a stronger impact. Pastels and tints soften the effects of the main color, while shades and tones subdue or lessen the effects of the main hue. Put children in the power seat and use color combining for their benefit and for their own self-empowerment. Have fun exploring and experimenting with color combinations!

The colors that children enjoy wearing not only reveal their unique personality, but also their emotional make-up and physical condition. Color selections can change daily according to their mood, a given situation or if they are recovering from an illness.You can have greater insight and understanding of their development, mood and overall personality by the colors they most enjoy wearing.

COLOR TYPES

NEON

Neon or day glow colors reflect the brightest rays of the sun and have the most exciting effect of all color types. The brilliance and *sunsation* of these vividly blinding colors is ultra stimulating to the senses. The fluorescent colors are visually captivating and are distinguishable at a greater distance than any other color types. These are the action-packed colors that evoke a sense of fun, adventure, excitement and spontaneity. Combined with highly contrasting black their effect is immensely intensified and more striking. Next to white, their glowing radiance is greatly increased. Neon colors are playful, festive and highly visible. Dress children in neon colors to be noticed in a crowd.

SOLAR COLORS

These are the true vibrant colors of the rainbow as seen in nature. Colors that are purely saturated without a tint of white or a shade of black help evoke a positive disposition and increase self-esteem. Solar colors are lively and stimulating to the senses. Wearing vivid hues lifts the spirits and evokes a stronger effect more than any other color types. Others will take notice of children and pay attention to what they have to say, when wearing these light-hearted colors.

PASTELS AND TINTS

Pastels are colors that contain a large amount of white and are the lightest form of a color. Tints are colors that contain white and are more saturated in hue than pastels. The sweet and gentle quality of pastels and tints soften the effects of the main color. Pastels are considered spiritual colors that evoke a sense of weightlessness, buoyancy and lightness. There is more light reflected from pastels. The vibrations are subtle and celestial. Dress children in pastels to mellow them out, to exude their beauty and personal charm and to elicit kindness and gentleness from others.

TONES AND SHADES

Colors that are mixed with gray are tones. Colors that contain black are shades. Tones have a dulling effect and diminish or subdue the effects of the particular hue. Tones evoke a sense of moodiness. Shades appear heavy and evoke sophistication, conservatism and a serious approach to situations. Wear muted shades on children when they need serious adjustments to a particular stiuation, and tones when they need to appear a bit conventional.

MONOCHROMATIC

Monochromatic is the combination of one or more pastels, tints, shades, or tones of the same color. This is one of the most pleasing and balanced color combinations. Since one hue dominates the entire color scheme it gives the feeling of being safe. Dressing children in variations of the same color-tints or shades etc. always has a harmonious and captivating appearance. For example children may have a need to learn about and respect the ecology around them. Wearing a dark green with mint, or emerald green with sea green conveys the message even stronger and clearer than if they were to wear green with a neutral or another color. Monochromatic colors are tasteful and have a greater impact and more power in conveying a specific message.

METALLIC

Rather than absorb light like black, or reflect light like white, iridescent and **metallic** colors scatter light. This is why they appear dazzling and sparkling to the eyes. The interplay of colors and the dynamic color changes represents the passage of life through the course of time; the dance of life. As children spiral into the space-age life style, the metallic and silvery gray tones will become more popular and prominent in their clothing and commercial accessories. Simplicity in design and form will be more marketable and have more mass appeal. As life becomes more complex, chiildren will tend to strive for simplicity. This space-age trend which has already begun, will be even more dramatic in the year 2001. With advanced technology and computers integrated into children's daily routine, color choices will become more cosmic and iridescent in all areas.

METALLIC COLOR EFFECTS

These are more detached and impersonal in their effect. They evoke excitement, enticement and attraction. They may sparkle the children's inner child with their awe and beauty. Overuse of this color type can become gaudy and over-bearing.

WARM METALS

Gold - warming in its effects, its colors range from white, glowing yellow and slight pink to soft green. Besides being highly attractive and ornamental to the wearer, it has a strengthening influence upon the body.

Copper - when polished, is warm in nature. It has been known to protect the physical body and have healing benefits for arthritis. It can stimulate enthusiasm and a zest for life. In its aging state, it turns green, adding a coolness to its warmth. Its effects are outstanding for healing and balancing the body.

COOL METALS

Silver - cool in nature and impersonal in appearance, silver has a stabilizing effect on the body and the emotions. In its tarnished state it becomes more neutralized and less effective.

Gray Metals - pewter, nickel, tin and all dull or silvery metals are neutral in appearance. They need bright or deep colors to add life to their presence. Their boring, dull mechanical qualities make them less popular than silver and the warm metals.

METALLIC PALETTE

If children immensely enjoy and wear glitter, sequins, and **metallic** colors, they are a true futurist, ready to explore space and progress into a more advanced society. They are probably living in the future through the way they view life in general and how they interact with others. If they favor the warm metals, especially gold, their taste is refined; they prefer the exquisite and exciting things in life. However, if they prefer silver over gold, they also enjoy the same but with less flash and more imagination. The dull gray metallics are generally not appealing to children.

IRIDESCENT

There is very little known about the **iridescent** colors. In nature these enchanting hues exist in abundance in sea life, insects and birds. The beauty of an opal, a peacock feather, or a tropical fish has fascinated and charmed children's universal inner appreciation. Seemingly from another world, these brilliant colors flirt with the children's inner dimension of their entire being. They express the ethereal side of existence, the dream state, the altered state of consciousness, speaking to the spiritual interior of children. This brilliant and radiant myriad of changing hues appear surreal.

IRIDESCENT PALETTE

If children favor the **iridescent** colors, they are definitely interested in other worlds of existence and enjoy using and exploring their imagination. They appreciate the magical and mystical aspects of life and are not afraid to explore a new dimension of life or altered state. They may be intrigued by their existence and are curious of the powers of the universe that brought them to earth. Meditation and understanding metaphysical realities are natural to them. Possibly they are developing or becoming more aware of their psychic abilities and spiritual purpose.

RAINBOW PALETTE

RED PALETTE

Red is the ultimate color for physical action, conquest and vitality. Children's personalities are fully animated when they wear red. They appear ardent and motivated toward success with a zest for life. The lively intensity of red helps them become assertive in situations with people.

Pink is a pastel of red and **rose** is a tint of red. Rosy pink is rejuvenating. Children who favor pink/rosey pink want to be treated with kindness and affection. Pink exudes physical gentleness, tender love, youthfulness and softness. They desire to be cuddled and pampered like a baby. Pink weakens an aggressive nature.

Burgundy is a tone and **crimson** is a shade of **red**. Both are reenergizing. The darker the shade the more subdued the desire for control of aggression. Children who prefer these colors handle their aggressive behavior and selfish desires maturely. They evoke an adventurous spirit with reason and practicality.

ORANGE PALETTE

Orange is the color of sociability and projects a fun and gregarious nature. It stimulates a sense of humor and lively conversation and helps children look at the bright side of a situation and relationship. Orange is stimulating both to the mind, capturing spiritual and intellectual wisdom, and to the body through increasing the appetite. The lighter tones of peach, salmon, coral and apricot adds an attractive glow to all skin tones and projects comfort and warmth in social settings. The darker shades like rust, or tones like brownish hues, evoke a sense of social stability and a friendly stable personality.

Peach and **Apricot** are pastels of Orange. **Coral** and **Salmon** are tints of Orange. Especially peach and salmon project social grace, charm, diplomacy and a warm personality. They are gently persuasive and spiritually wise. They evoke self-control in situations with fair play toward others. All of these are the best colors for friendly social gatherings and in making a positive, memorable impression.

Burnt Orange is a shade of orange and **Rust** is a tone of Orange. Orange shades and tones project an earthy love for life and a controlled sense of fun.

YELLOW PALETTE

Yellow is the color of upliftment and intellectual stimulation. Yellow projects a positive nature. Children who prefer yellow have mental determination to manifest their future desires and find solutions to current problems for new and improved possibilities. They are studious, inquisitive and adept at organizing. Yellow radiates positive regard toward the self and others. Yellow helps relationships to become stress free.

Lemon is a pastel of yellow. Children who favor pale yellow are visionaries with exceptional foresight into the future.

29

They are innovative and hold to their own ideas. They are fun with a sunny disposition and understanding and patient with those less intelligent then themselves.

Umber and **mustard** are tones and **ocher** is a shade of yellow. Children who favor these colors are serious about learning and enjoy exploring the future. They project a positive, mature and realistic personality.

GREEN PALETTE

Green is the color of will-power and self-determination. Green helps children overcome opposition and remain independent in spite of difficulties. Green spurs them on to recognition and achievement. Green is commanding without being demanding.

Mint is a pastel and **sea green** a tint of green. Children who prefer light green need to maintain a sense of well-being even under negative circumstances. They project a gentle and mellow nature. Green tints evoke a steady commitment to projects and relationships.

Forest green is a shade and **olive green** is a tone of green. Children who prefer forest green are deeply committed to their word or promises made. They project a love for nature and traditional family values and relationships. They are reliable and can shoulder difficult responsibilities with a calm mind and self-assurance. If they prefer olive they approach life with a narrow viewpoint or a one sided vision. They camouflage their true feelings behind a quiet demeanor.

BLUE PALETTE

Blue is the relationship color. Children preferring blue express a serene, peaceful and harmonious nature with a desire to learn and please others. They are considerate and caring toward others. Mutuality and gentle persuasion are their keys to success.

Powder blue (faded blue jeans) is a pastel and **robin's egg blue** is a tint of blue. Most children prefer light blue. They express a desire to involve themselves in a new relationship or a group endeavor. They evoke an open and compromising spirit and use gentle persuasion. Robin's egg blue helps to build self-confidence and to express a charismatic presence.

Cobalt blue is a shade and **country blue** is a tone of blue. Children who favor the darker blues are in spiritual search for inner harmony and a secure relationship with family members and/or a parental figure. They evoke sincerity, mutual understanding, a calm and controlled disposition.

INDIGO PALETTE

Indigo represents humanity, groups, organizations and multiple relationships. Indigo stimulates the superconscious, the connection to a universal source, to all humanity. Children who prefer indigo are honorable, dignified and highly principled. They live their inner truth and are independent.

Periwinkle is a pastel and **baby blue** is a tint of indigo. Children who favor light indigo have a need to experience their connection to their Higher Self, the Divine spiritual power within them. They project a sincere and conscientious attitude. Soft indigo personalities appear aloof and spiritually searching.

Navy and **royal blue** are shades and **slate blue** is a tone of indigo. Children of these color types are traditional, spiritually inspired and are loyal and devoted to a cause or special interest group. Dark indigo indicates contentment and tranquility. They are happy remaining with the status quo.

VIOLET PALETTE

Violet is the color of the creative imagination, magnetic charm and personal magic. Purple and violet stimulate the intuitive faculties and spiritual awareness. Children who prefer purple and magenta like to stand out as unique individuals. They are super sensitive, highly imaginative and seek identification with someone they admire.

Lavender is a pastel and **orchid, lilac** and bright **purple** are tints of violet. Children favoring light violet are extremely sensitive, unique and original with rich imaginations. The supernatural and other worlds interest them. They project a sense of personal magic and quiet charisma. They follow their strong intuition over logic.

31

Mauve and **mulberry** are tones and **plum** is a shade of violet. Preference for these colors indicate children who can be fanatical thinkers and judgmental of others with tendencies toward inertia. They have a serious approach to problems and explore creative solutions. They project a greater concern for the spiritual or psychological over the physical and material. Preference for mauve indicates originality, sophistication and a bent toward a modern style.

WHITE PALETTE

White is impartial in nature. White by itself is void of emotions. It reflects light and repels negativity. Children preferring white as a dominant color indicate a need to totally control their space and feel safe from unpleasant people and situations. Worn with other colors as an accent white adds flair and enhances the dominant color. White stimulates the positive effects of vivid or pure hues. Wearing white as an accent with vibrant or deep colors gives a polished and neat appearance. White further softens the gentle and subtle effects of pastels adding style and grace. White sharply contrasts shades or deep hues, demanding attention from others. Ivory, cream, and bone are tones of white. As an accent with other colors these white variations add sophistication, elegance, and subtle definition.

GRAY PALETTE

Gray is the color to hide behind or to conceal something. As a dominant color gray allows children's true feelings to be hidden or concealed in the meaning of the accent colors. It is the best color to wear with variations of blue under severe emotionally or physically taxing situations. Gray is neutralizing, void of personality, impersonal, implies noninvolvement and expresses elegance and soft sophistication. Most children dislike gray.

BLACK PALETTE

Black projects sophistication, mysterious power and strength of one's own views and convictions. Black indicates a refusal to change or adapt to new circumstances. As a dominant color, black weakens the effect of the accent color. Black can project an uncaring, uninterested, and unhappy disposition. Black is best worn as an accent color with highly contrasting bright and vivid hues for children. The impact of black on other colors is strong and extreme and is highly dramatic.

BROWN PALETTE

Brown projects a sense of security, stability, reliability and physical comfort. Brown is the color for children who are service-oriented and like to please and help others. Brown represents convention and tradition.

Tan is a tint and **beige** a pastel of brown. Children who prefer brown tints project a warm personality and are people oriented. They desire moderation and safety in everything they do. Tan or beige with cool colors- green and blue express a calm, subtle and comfortable feeling. Light brown with the warm hues- orange, red and yellow evoke their dramatic and dynamic qualities in a more subtle and socially acceptable manner.

Taupe is a tone and **chocolate brown** is a shade of brown. Children who prefer these colors desire worldly comforts and can be obsessive about their needs. They project a non-committed attitude and can hide their true feelings through isolation and a stubborn attitude. The darker forms of brown with blues and greens express a helpful and considerate attitude toward other's needs. Reds, oranges, and yellows with the darker shades of brown express a cordial and demonstrative personality in a respectable manner.

CHILDREN'S APPAREL

Specific colors children wear can help modify or encourage a particular behavior and enhance an aspect of their personality. Ideally it is best to give them a choice of colors available in their wardrobe. Children express their own unique color style and paint their own personal color portrait.

RED

Red invigorates, helps build self-confidence and attracts attention. Red stimulates physical activity and helps overweight children lose weight. Red helps to revitalize! The various light tints of pink and bright rosey pink gives cuddles, affection, and pampering. The dark shades of burgandy and bright cranberry set a serious tone for formal occasions.

Red/Orange - Stimulates hyperactivity and spontaneity. A great combination for sport teams and energetic activities.

Red/Yellow - Influences enthusiasm, self-confidence and optimism. Gives an intense drive to achieve goals. A great combination for individual competitive sports.

Red/Green - Projects a domineering and self-assured personality. This combination, especially rose pink with mint or emerald green express a strong will and a lovable disposition.

Red/Blue - rosy red with deep blue helps in situations that require benevolence and acceptance from others. Burgundy with navy blue implies sophistication and helps evoke maturity and a serious compromising nature.

Red/Indigo projects a dynamic and courageous leader and expresses individuality. Red with navy or royal blue helps in a leadership role to impel others to action. Pink with light indigo influences gentle persuasion among family or peers.

Red/Violet projects a magical and magnetic personality.

Red/Brown express enthusiasm and contentment as a family member.

Red/Black express a freedom loving personality and a dare devil attitude. A great combination for a time of fun and excitement.

Red/Gray helps inhibit reckless behavior and impulsive action. Gives the appearance of an outward sense of security if inwardly uncertain or undecided. Excellent colors to wear in situations that require acts of courage and self-confidence, such as stage fright or giving a presentation in front of a group.

Red/White express bossiness and intense desire to be in total control of desires and ambitions. They project an aggressive and intimidating personality. This combination demands attention.

34

ORANGE

Orange stimulates socialization in a cheerful and amiable way. Peach enhances the expression of style and grace in appearance. Orange and its lighter tones add a cheerful glow and express self assurance, and self assertion.

Orange/Red helps influence backward or shy children to develop social skills and to overcome timidity.

Orange/Yellow enhances a friendly disposition, gregarious interaction with others and attracts new friends.

Orange/Green projects a humorous and fun loving image. Light orange, peach, salmon, and apricot with a darker or deeper green express social grace and congeniality.

Orange/Blue in the deeper subdued shades of rust with navy blue express a friendly and responsible disposition in formal situations. Peach with deep blue helps in congenial social affairs and open family discussions.

Orange/Indigo and peach with periwinkle express a congenial and trustworthy disposition.

Orange/Violet express originality in unique ways and projects the image of a harmless rebel. Coral with purple or deep violet helps stimulate the imagination of children in a group setting.

Orange/Brown projects a warm personality with a down to earth attitude. Peach, coral or salmon with tan or beige expresses congenial interaction in social gatherings with peers.

Orange/Gray projects a mature, fun-loving and delightful personality that uses descretion with others. Orange with charcoal gray helps tone down a boisterous or loud personality.

Orange/Black expresses amicability in a negative situation and helps social acceptance by society or peers. Peach, coral and salmon with black projects congeniality and personal power in large social gathering.

Orange/White expresses emotional openness, spontaneity, adventurousness and a playful dispostion.

YELLOW

Yellow projects a happy and carefree nature, warmth and cheerfulness, and brings attention to children's unique qualities and outstanding traits. A dash of yellow creates a healthy glow.

Yellow/Red projects the overachiever image and the courage to stand alone in a new situation.

Yellow/Orange expresses a warm and outgoing nature and positive self-confidence and stimulates open problem-solving discussions with groups.

Yellow/Green projects a love for individual freedom, self-growth and recognition.They are persuasive and help influence others to adapt to new ideas and a balanced lifestyle.

Yellow/Blue projects a positive, self-accepting image and builds self-esteem.The wearer craves attention from parental figures and enjoys being the center of attention.

Yellow/Indigo exudes positive assurance and a cheerful attitude toward others. Yellow with navy or royal blue helps to plan future goals with family members. Pale yellow with navy or indigo stimulates mental motivation.

Yellow/Violet expresses a fun and sunny disposition. Helps to motivate spiritual growth and psychological insights.

Yellow/Brown expresses an alert and inventive mind.Yellow with dark brown projects a sharp mind and a stable personality. Lemon with tan projects an open mind and a friendly disposition.

Yellow/Black helps to make a positive change and focus on serious matters under difficult circumstances. Aids in memorization and comprehension of difficult subjects.

Yellow/Gray projects a sophisticated style and mature demeanor. Helps mental concentration and clarity to focus on studies and problem solving.

Yellow/White helps to uplift the spirits from negative emot-ions and exudes warmth and cheer. Excellent combination when visiting the depressed or physically ill.

GREEN

Green projects practicality, nurturing nature, balance, status and will-power. It is commanding without being demanding. Its balancing properties are comfortable in all seasons. Green greatly improves your health.

Green/Red - helps to concentrate and focus energy in order to single-handedly accomplish tasks. A great combination for physical outdoor work, such as yard work or gardening.

Green/Orange - projects a mature adventurous and gregar-ious spirit. Mint green with coral, peach or salmon harmon-izes the mind and body. Enhances concern for the total welfare of others. For selfless acts toward others deep green with peach tones is best.

Green/Yellow - expresses a harmonious nature in the attempt to bridge the gap between others. Deeper tones of green with golden yellow helps to successfully instruct peers on new projects. Peer leadership is emphasized.

Green/Blue - wants to make a favorable impression and receive proper recognition for abilities and talents. These colors influence others in a group or family setting.

Green/Indigo - projects a cool, calm disposition with quiet self-assurance. Emerald green with royal blue and vivid indigo expresses physical balance and mental calmness.

Green/Violet - expresses originality and a need to impress upon others that this is a special personality. Deep rich greens, especially emerald green with lavender or deep violets balance the physical body and their psyche.

Green/Brown - projects the ability to overcome difficulties with unwanted responsibilities. A need to express self pride and maintain a sense of security is paramount. Deep shades of green with tan or beige elicit calmness and comfort in long and strenuous group or family activities.

Green/Gray - evokes a need to build self-esteem and make an impression on others despite unfavorable circumstances. A cool and calm disposition is expressed outwardly, while having mixed feelings inwardly. This combination in all color types expresses a conservative disposition in financial and family affairs.

Green/Black - indicates an overwhelming self-will to prove immense personal power and lack of any weakness; a desire to be the center of attention inwardly, while projecting a conservative and cautious nature outwardly. Deep tones of green with black aids in enlisting help from others.

Green/White is kindhearted and nurturing. Light green exudes mutual tenderness and contentment at home.

BLUE

Blue expresses a charming and pleasing nature, and improves self-moderation and self-assurance. Blue relaxes the entire body and has an equalizing effect on the energy level.

Blue/Red - expresses a love of family and community. Stimulates dynamic group interaction.

Blue/Orange and aqua with light peach or coral helps to balance personal needs with those of others.

Blue/Yellow helps to harmoniously work with others toward a mutual goal. Attracts attention to persoanlity traits.

Blue/Green helps balance the physical body and calm the mind.The deeper shades help harmonize stressful situations.

Blue/Indigo and peacock or aqua with royal blue projects a sense of beauty and harmony. This combination is popular and attractive for dealing with groups.

Blue/Violet and aqua with purple stimulates creative ideas for artistic projects. Lavender with peacock or cobalt blue expresses devotion to a spiritual/religious group.

Blue/Brown expresses outward indifference while inwardly warm. The darker hues project a fear of separation and loneliness. Light aqua, teal, or peacock with tan or beige attract acceptance and warmth from others.

Blue/Black and deep blue or cobalt with black expresses a mysterious nature and hidden emotions.

Blue/Gray expresses insecurity with decision-making. Peacock blue with gray helps in educational or group settings that require good judgment and objectivity.

Blue/White projects a charismatic, inspiring, and self-reliant nature. Helps mental clarity and proper motivation to achieve goals. Attracts admiration for achievements. Peacock blue projects self-confidence and a positive influence on others.

INDIGO

Indigo expresses a conscientious and intuitive nature. Royal blue helps children feel secure and included among groups. Indigo portrays spiritual/religious devotion and a serious and loyal image.

Indigo/Red indicate impartiality and responsible leadership. Royal blue with pink projects your love and devotion to family members or a group.

Indigo/Orange and navy with rusty orange projects an image of fidelity and trust to a person or cause.

Indigo/Yellow and navy with pale yellow stimulates intellectual brain-storming and time management. Projects a studious nature.

Indigo/Green and royal blue with bright green is practical and conservative. Light green with indigo projects a kind-hearted and caring nature toward others.

Indigo/Blue and vivid indigo with peacock blue expresses charisma in a leadership position among peers.

Indigo/Violet and indigo with lavender expresses a spiritual attitude and helps to plan your future projects. Deep purple with bright indigo is ideal for a religious or spiritual celebration.

Indigo/Gray projects a reserved and detached disposition. Deep indigo or navy with silvery gray helps to plan future educational goals.

Indigo/Brown expresses a friendly nature toward others in a reserved and calm fashion. Indigo and tan /beige help with congeniality in group activities. Navy with beige projects harmony and a complacent and pleasant nature.

Indigo/Black projects the image of an aloof, detached and withdrawn personality. Deep indigo or navy with black expresses a great need to calm nervous tension.

Indigo/White projects a pure and innocent nature. Deep indigo or navy and white helps harmony and compatability with everyone in group interactions.

VIOLET

Violet helps to endure an undesirable situation with inner strength and reflects a noble and genuine character. Bright magenta and vivid purple express the unique and fascinating aspects of children's personalities and expands their personal magnetism.

Violet/Red expresses an imaginative nature and originality . Lilac and pink portrays a delicate and sensitive nature.

Violet/Orange expresses a sense of humor and artistic talents. Lavender with soft peach evokes a celebrative and humorous disposition. This is a popular and fun combination for younger children to wear.

Violet/Yellow and lavender or lilac with pale yellow attracts sensitivity and positive regard from others. A favorite color combination in infant's wear.

Violet/Green and purple with turquoise and rich green adds flair to mundane tasks and helps pursue studies.

Violet /Blue and purple with aqua and any tints of blue help inspire the creative imagination with the arts. Violet with deep blue help to soothe the mind and relax the body.

Violet/Indigo tints like periwinkle with lavender enhance spiritual judgment and stimulate the creative imagination to problem-solve with family or groups.

Violet/Brown projects a congenial, warm personality and subtle individuality. Lavender and beige express a calm and comfortable disposition.

Violet/Black evokes mystery and a magical charm. Purple with black projects a sense of dignity and power.

Violet/Gray projects a delicate personality that requires extra special treatment and sensitivity from others. Violet with light gray or lavender with charcoal gray expresses refinement and a touch of individuality.

Violet/White stimulates the imagination and soothes nervous tension.

COLOR COMBINATIONS FOR ACTIVITIES, SPORTS AND TOYS

SPECTRUM IN YELLOW

Yellow is the color of the radiant sun - the source of life itself! Its brilliance and welcoming warmth cheers the heart, delights the mind, and enlightens the spirit. Its powerful and positive influence upon you can bring personal fulfillment in your life.

Colors in combination affect each other and together make a particular impact that also emits an unconscious message. The colors of play toys, learning tools, sporting goods and objects in the environment influence children. Experiment with these various color combinations for specific reasons and particular outcomes. Functional color can influence children's behavior and enhance their mood.

Color studies in the field of neuropsychology indicate that objects that are colored have a greater cue to memory than uncolored things. Children who are alert and inquisitive in nature are attracted and responsive to bright saturated colors especially in the early years of development. Experiment with different color schemes and note the difference it makes with children.

SPORTS AND ACTIVITIES

RED

Packed with power and pure energy red is the most invigorating color for sports and activities.

Red/Orange are very stimulating for the muscular system and the nervous system. Both stimulate hyperactivity and spontaneity. They are excellent for peak performance in competitive sports that also require sportsmanship and fair play.

Red/Yellow's intense and hot combination are both mentally and physically overpowering. Their intensity grabs children's attention and is favorable for sports and activities that require speed and fast decisions, such as ice hockey, roller blading and skiing.

Red/Green are complementary contrasts. Red indicates the spirit of love and green the color for life and together are dynamic opposites. A great combination for outdoor activities, such as yard work or gardening.

Red/Blue are popular dynamic team colors that invigorate and help to influence cooperation among team members. Excellent for a team leadership role, these colors help to attract attention and have group appeal.

Red/Indigo are fantastic colors for team loyalty and devotion. Excellent for group activity where trust, fast action and good judgment among group members is required.

Red/Black are packed with intense power and energy! Together these colors stimulate a dare devil tendency and help instill courage to do invigorating tasks. For example, they are excellent for high diving in swimming competition.

Red/Gray helps to focus energy and control risk taking and impulsive action. These popular team colors evoke serious fan participation at games and help team members direct tremendous physical aggression and speed toward specific tasks. Excellent colors for situations that require acts of courage and to handle an emergency. Excellent for daring sports such as football, wrestling and gymnastics.

Red/Silver enhances swift movement with style and grace. Ideal for winter festivities and activities like jogging, ice skating and hockey.

Red/White stimulates assertiveness and helps the wearer to be in total control of directing energy and accomplishing tasks at hand. This combination demands attention, can be intimidating and helps courageous leadership. Favorable colors for wrestling, baseball, soccer, and jogging teams.

ORANGE

The physically and mentally stimulating, friendly orange is a popular color for sport teams. Orange is the best color for positive team spirit and cooperative team effort. Orange influences camaraderie, fan enthusiasm and is best for any group activity, which involves group achievement.

Orange/Red are overpowering and fast-moving. This is a great combination for sports that require speed and dependent interaction among team members, such as soccer and basketball.

Orange/Yellow enhance positive team cooperation. Together they express mental stimulation and positive team spirit. Excellent for group debate teams and outdoor games.

Orange/Violet express a wildly free nature and are best for fun and playful activities.

Orange/Brown helps to project a warm personality with a down to earth attitude. Excellent combination for congenial interaction in social gatherings with children or groups.

Orange/Gray helps with group activities that require self-control and a serious demeanor. This combination is amicable, while being discerning toward others. Helps to tone down a boisterous or loud crowd. Good for groups during sports practice.

Orange/Black helps to project congeniality in a serious or negative situation and aids in social acceptance by society and/or peers. Gives a friendly disposition in a position of power and authority over children or as the head of a large social gathering.

Orange/White projects a sense of adventure, spontaneity and safe fun. Stimulates enjoyable and playful interaction with others in a fun way. Great for successful outdoor group outings and sports.

YELLOW

Yellow is mentally tantalizing and helps in situations that require quick decision making and a positive attitude. It is the ideal color for individual and team spirit and mental activities, where recalling and following specific steps are required, such as routines for gymnastics, dance, or Thai Chi. Yellow is also excellent when precise sequential directions are essential, for example, operating a computer program.

Yellow(Gold)/Green expresses positive team spirit, good sportsmanship and the will-power to win. Excellent combination for group activities that require instruction and guidance. Helps to create a cheerful disposition for a group leader for peer teaching.

Yellow(Gold)/Blue project a positive image, helps create harmony and cooperation among group members and promotes a cohesiveness for group goals. Excellent for activities that require emotional and intellectual balance.

Yellow/Violet stimulates the mind and the imagination. Excellent for competitive games like chess and word games.

Yellow/Indigo expresses positive assurance and a cheerful attitude toward others. Stimulates creative brain-storming for future planning and problem-solving. Helps assist family members reach future goals. Excellent for board games.

Yellow/Brown expresses open-mindedness and physical comforts. Helps deep concentration and an unyielding attitude in pursuit of goals. Stimulates an alert and inventive mind and stable actions. Excellent for activities that require mental agility and physical stability, such as fast moving and challenging computer and virtual reality games.

Yellow/Black helps project a cheerful disposition and concealed emotions. Stimulates a serious approach to future goals and success. Stimulates mental concentration and strong mental powers. Excellent for mental board games such as chess.

Yellow/Gray helps to approach new situations with caution. Expresses an open-minded and progressive viewpoint with controlled emotions. Excellent for activities that require important decisions and adjustments such as structured, timed games, contests and tests.

Yellow /White helps exude warmth and cheerfulness toward others and a positive attitude toward future events. Excellent for outdoor winter sports for visibility and a happy disposition.

GREEN

Green is cautious, conservative, commanding and practical. Packed with will-power, green expresses balance and fairess. It is an ideal color for activities that require moderation, a sense of timing, caring for others and instructing others. Emerald and bright green are excellent for peer coaching; green helps children be in command of a situation and to exercise their will-power. Its soothing properties and neutralizing vibrations are comfortable in all seasons and situations. Green greatly improves the health.

46

Green/Indigo directs energy in a cool, calm and collected manner. These popular sportswear colors evoke quiet assurance and commanding disposition. The will-power of the wearer is directed toward group or family goals and is helpful among peers. Great colors for sports like bowling.

Green/Violet is inspiring and mentally and physically healing. Excellent for playing musical instruments, where creativity and artistry is focused on soothing and nurturing the body, mind and spirit.

Green/Brown represents a connection to nature and helps the wearer overcome difficulties with unwanted responsibilities and reserves and directs the wearer's energy efficiently. Light green with tan or beige expresses self-pride, a sense of security and dignity. Expresses calmness and comfort in long and strenuous group or family activities. Very good for gardening and all outdoor activities and sports such as golf and tennis.

Green/Gray helps build the wearer's self-esteem and make an impression on others despite unfavorable circumstances. Projects a cool and calm disposition outwardly, while having mixed feelings inwardly. This combination in all color types expresses a conservative disposition in family affairs.

Green/Black expresses the desire to be the center of attention inwardly, while projecting a conservative and cautious disposition outwardly. Enlists the help of others to assist the wearer in achieving a common goal.

Green/White is considerate, supportive and helpful toward team/family members. The wearer demonstrates sincerity and commitment to group goals and exhibits genuine love and concern toward the family or team. Excellent for home projects involving the family and outdoor sports such as golf.

BLUE

Blue improves self-moderation and self-assurance. Wearing blue relaxes the entire body and has an equalizing effect on your energy.

Blue/Indigo expresses self-reliance, independence, self-confidence and aloofness. The brighter tones are excellent for activities that require centering of the emotions and concentration of posture such as yoga, swimming and isometric and low impact exercising.

Blue/Violet creates positive effects on the mind, spiritual self, and the emotions. The lighter tones of blue and purple are best for activities, playtime and the arts where the creative imagination is stimulated and participation is alone or in a group.

Blue/Brown express outward indifference and inward warmth. Light/bright blue and beige are best in situations where acceptance, trust and understanding are needed toward achieving mutual goals, such as meditation and group/family discussions.

Blue/Black desires peace, affection, consideration and relaxation at all costs. Vivid blue with black is great for bedtime story telling.

Blue/Gray is dependent on interaction with others to replace boredom and lack of personal interests. Bright blue projects a secure personality that hides indecisiveness and insecurities. Best for activities that require good judgment and cohesive group action, such as working on projects for a group cause.

Blue/Silver expresses charismatic group spirit and positive group identity.

Blue/White is influential, inspiring, and self-reliant. Motivates the wearer toward achievement of goals for outcomes of admiration and respect from others. Excellent for academic competition/studies, the arts (dance, music, visual art) and sports such as swimming and baseball.

INDIGO

Indigo projects loyalty, a calm disposition, spirit of compromise and fair play. It is the best color for activities that require a serious and conscientious approach and unifies a group. Royal blue is one of the most popular colors among groups.

Indigo/Violet (purple) expresses deep contemplation, inventive imagination and commitment to a project or group.

Best for an activity that unifies or brings things or ideas together, such as group/family decision making and choir and play practice.

Indigo/Gray is realistic, reserved and impersonal. Helps to bring into focus group creative ideas. Excellent for individual research and intellectual discovery for a team goal, such as a science project that would rely on a specific role for each individual.

Indigo/Silver (Royal/electric blue) expresses a unified and humanitarian image and is deeply committed to future goals of a group/family.

Indigo/Brown expresses equality, respect, warmth and fair treatment to everyone. Royal/electric blue with light beige is best for groups performing service for the community, such as volunteer groups.

Indigo/Black (royal/electric blue) projects tremendous power within a spiritual, humanitarian and or special interest group. Best for working on group projects alone and in a peaceful and quiet setting. Excellent for meditation or story telling before bedtime to combat insomnia.

Indigo/White projects loyalty and dedication to an idealistic philosophy of a group and support of its plans for the future. Excellent for organizations that require harmony, unification and future directing. For example the girl/boy scouts, peer volunteers that help special interests groups, and/or school sponsorships.

VIOLET

Violet is great for mental endurance and inner strength in difficult and challenging activities, such as downhill skiing and bike racing. The royal purple stimulates the imagination and aids in clever moves for game playing. Magenta and bright purple express personal magnetism, the fantasy world and individuality and add flair to mundane tasks

Violet/Brown (purple/tan) is amicable, creative and grounding. Bright purple and beige helps the child to be comfortable and cooperative with others while creating arts and crafts in a group.

Violet/Black is mysteriously dramatic, magical and imaginative. Magenta or vivid purple with black stimulate daydreaming. Activities that enhance the child to fantasize different characters and pretend, such as play acting, dance and art.

Violet/Gray projects sensitivity, formality and refinement. Purple and light gray is best for creative activities such as the performing arts- playing in a band, singing in choir etc.

Violet/Silver is dignified, futuristic and artistically formal. Bright purple is regal and formal. Magenta and lavender are enchanting and magical. Excellent for activities that stimulate futuristic ideas and inventions such as science fiction story telling or creative writing.

Violet/White expresses spirituality, royal purity and natural (unadulterated) creativity. Magenta and lavender stimulate a fresh imagination for making spontaneous creations. Some expressive activities include finger painting, doodling, song writing and improvisational music or dance.

TOYS AND VEHICLES

The color children choose for bicycles, skateboards, skates, athletic shoes (symbolic of vehicles for children) and toy air planes, cars, balls and trucks etc., outwardly reflects their inner needs and personality. Only the **color preferred** for a vehicle or a toy applies to the information below.

Red - Children who prefer a red toy or vehicle indicate they want adventure, excitement and fun. Red is the color of energy and speed. It is the quickest moving vibration of all the colors. A bright red car, boat, bicycle or train, even when standing still, appears to be moving. The brighter the red, the more dynamic and daring is the child's interaction with the toy or approach behind the wheel of a vehicle. Favoring **maroon, burgundy**, or more deep and dark subdued tones of red, tones down the aggressive expression and is more self-controlled. Choosing **pink** or shades of **rose** reveals the child's need to be pampered and the desire to stand out as an individual with unique taste.

Orange - The vivid and bright appearance of orange stands out easily in most surroundings. Preferring orange marks children as individuals who express a carefree and fun attitude and enjoy sharing toys and playtime with others. They exude a friendly disposition toward others and are considerate of their needs. They may use their vehicle or toy to socialize and express a little flash. Children while operating a vehicle will speed with discretion under safe circumstances. **Peach** is preferred by the diplomatic socialite, the tender hearted, and one who enjoys playing with peers.

Yellow - is the brightest color of the spectrum and it is the harshest for the eyes to observe. Because of its remarkable visibility, it is an excellent color for boats and all small vehicles such as skateboards and bikes. Children who favor yellow toys and vehicles are a whirlwind of energy whose keen imagination sees endless possibilities with their toys. They are mentally alert and like to be noticed by others. Selecting pale yellow or cream, indicates highly intellectual children who enjoy being progressive in style.

Green - is the most soothing color to perceive, especially emerald and vivid tones. Children's preference for green vehicles reveals a practical and conservative approach to operating it. They are cautious while operating a bike and express courtesy toward peers. The more brilliant and vivid the green the more self-controlled, genuinely caring and determined children are in nature. Children favoring **olive** and subdued greens like **forest** or **hunter green**, tend to be introverted and are not interested in being noticed. They are followers or quiet leaders and passive in nature. If **lime green** is their favorite, they desire to be noticed, enjoy attention and dynamic interaction with their peers.

Neon/Vibrant Green - is one of the most popular colors. This exciting vivid color is pleasant to the eyes and noticeable in all seasons. Children who prefer neon green toys and vehicles are peppy, proud and positive. They literally feel good and exhilarated while riding a neon green bike, skates etc. or playing with vibrant green toys.

Blue - is the most pleasing color to the eyes and one of the most popular color choices for a vehicle, especially a bicycle. Blue is one of the slowest vibrations in the spectrum; as a result, blue vehicles give the optical illusion of moving slower

51

than they actually are. Children who prefer the vivid or **neon metallic blue** have an eye for beauty and taste. Selecting a deeper or more subdued blue reflects their need for a calm, relaxing experience while operating the vehicle. These individuals tend to be easy going and will enjoy sharing toys with peers. Children favoring **powder blue** or **light metallic blue**, are complacent and passive in nature. They don't like to be in a rush and would rather patiently take their time. In general, selecting blue indicates a need for belonging and emotional security.

Neon/Vibrant Aqua - is one of the most attractive colors. Its high visibility in all weather conditions makes it a great color for vehicles. Children who favor vivid turquoise and deep aqua are vivacious and have an appreciation for beauty and design, and love to live in an enchanting world. This is a popular color choice for the poised and gracious driver. Toys this color are their cherished treasures.

Indigo - **navy** and vivid **cobalt blue** with a violet cast is usually selected as a trim or accent color for boats, aircraft, bicycles, etc. Children who favor this deep rich hue are ultra-conservative, traditional and responsible in nature. They are proud of their possessions and will take exceptional care of their toys and/or vehicles. They have a need to enjoy and appreciate their possessions and are loyal to their playmates.

Purple represents fantasy and magic. Children who prefer purple toys and skateboards etc. want to be recognized for their unique style and like to stand out among peers. They enjoy expressing their creative imagination and theatrical nature. They are accepting of their peers' differences and are very sensitive and tender hearted toward their peers.

Neon Magenta - Children who favor magenta have a whimsical and creative nature. They are usually flamboyant non-comformists and proud of it. They need to be different from everyone else. They are true individualists. Their toys and vehicles represent their magical fantasy play world. They are independent and can play happily by themselves. Often they have imaginary playmates and make excellent actors. They need to express their originality and unique style.

White - Children preferring white vehicles and toys, are perfectionists and need to feel important. They are meticulous about the appearance of their material possessions (toys, bike etc.). and rarely share them with their peers. They are very conscious of their social status. They can be cautious of new friends, preferring established friends as playmates and familiar surroundings. They are neat and stylish in appearance.

Gray/Silver - Preference for gray or **silver** toys and bikes, etc. indicates that children may feel impersonal and indifferent towards them and may not take proper care of them. Selecting silver tones reflects that they are practical and moderate in their habits or sloppy and careless. They like to have a routine existence, where everything has its own proper place and function. They tend to be realists in their outlook and exhibit self-control during playtime with others. They enjoy vehicles purely for their function.

Black - A preference for a black toy and/or vehicle reveals children's desire for power, luxury and material possessions. Culturally, black signifies sophistication and social importance. Black is sleek and mysterious in appearance. Children who favor black for a vehicle or toy are somewhat risk-taking and fearless in their approach to operating it. Black reflects children's need to be important and their desire for formality, dignity and style.

Brown - Brown, **beige**, and **tan** are the warm neutrals abundant in nature. Children who prefer brown for a toy and/or vehicle, need comfort, stability and security. Selecting an orange brown or rust vehicle or toy implies that they are unyielding in a given situation and like to play with the same playmates and like routine. A preference for brown tones reveals that they are honest, well mannered and direct with their playmates.They like to play the adult role. They can be stubborn and predictable in nature.

ENVIRONMENTAL EFFECTS

SPECTRUM IN GREEN

Green is the color of spring and all abundance of life. It is the essence of life vibrating in growth. Its subtle influence and effect upon you can be used to serve your every need. Add green in your life today.

PLAYROOM

All the bright and vivid colors of the rainbow are ideal for a children's playroom. The colors excite, energize and stimulate children toward adventure, fun and exploration. Add a particular color as a dominant hue or place colored objects in the room to enhance a particular mood or behavior.

PLAYGROUND AND OUTDOORS

The colors that are functional for safety measures are best suited for outdoor play facilities. The warm colors of red, orange and yellow and bright vivid purple are excellent for outdoor play facilities. For example a swing set that is yellow or orange with silver or gray is easiest for the eyes to see. These contrasting color combinations catch the eye and are visible in a natural setting. Overall bright yellow is highly recommended for the greatest contrast for all seasons.

COLORS FOR CHILDREN'S SURROUNDINGS

Red - Add a dash of red to the surroundings to stimulate creative activities and to revitalize the physical body. Red adds life and energy to a room.

Orange - Add orange to a room to stimulate the appetite and to create a friendly atmosphere. **Peach** is the most livable and charming color for the family room. It promotes thoughtfulness and consideration toward others and increases pleasant social interactions.

Yellow - Add yellow to brighten the children's play environment and study room to create a positive atmosphere for learning and relating to others. Even in small amounts, its glowing nature is stimulating to the mind and uplifts the spirit.

Green - Surround children with green for stability and comfort. Its spring-time quality livens a room like a breath of fresh air. Green is soothing to the eyes and subdues excitation. Accented with lighter tones, it is very pleasing to the senses. Add green plants to any room and feel refreshed!

Blue - A dominant blue color scheme calms the emotions, rests the body, and creates a sensitive and trusting atmosphere for children to relate to others. Light blue creates a spacious effect and dark blue a cooling effect. Surround children with blue to acquire peace of mind and emotional balance.

Indigo - Surround children with indigo for emotional tranquillity and to create harmony among family members and groups. It is an excellent color to help restore children's health and to recover from physical pain or a severe operation. It is best suited for the children's bedroom for deep and restive sleep.

Violet - Add tints of violet(lavendar) and purple (lilac) to children's surroundings for a unique touch, refinement and to enhance aesthetic beauty. Deeper and richer shades of violet are best for a meditation room. The warmer tones with more red stimulate creativity and enhance vivid fantasizing. Use magenta for sparkle and charm, and to create a festive atmosphere. Magenta is ideal for most celebrations.

White - Surround children with white to recover from a negative situation, to feel safe, to regain a positive attitude and to begin a new direction in life. White's stark quality gives the appearance that everything is new and clean.

Gray - Gray is best as an accent color to any surroundings. It is especially tasteful with warm pastel tones and gives a fashionable impression. Too much gray is not only drab, but very boring to look at. As an accent color it is a great color in environments where children need to study and concentrate on important details.

Black - Incorporating black as an accent in the children's environment adds a touch of simplicity and refinement. A dominantly black room is overpowering and can create a feeling of heaviness and depression.

Brown - A domination of brown (carpeting) in the children's environment creates a sense of security and earthy comfort. It's warm, neutrality evokes a feeling of safety and a sense of belonging. Various light tones - beige, tan and mushroom as accent colors with peach for a living room or dining room is welcoming and warm for children's interaction with others.

GENERAL COLOR LIGHTING

Red - The warm quality of red lights creates a tantilizing atmosphere for dining. Its desirable nature helps you enjoy eating and the sense of taste is livelier. Red stimulates creative activity and provides a warm glow during cold weather. **Pink** night lights are ideal for the children's bedroom. It stimulates positive dreams and emits a loving, affectionate and warm atmosphere.

Orange - Orange is stimulating to the palate and is best for social dining. **Peach** night lights provide a warm and subtle friendly glow for sleeping and for positive interaction among siblings who share a room.

Yellow - The warm affect of yellow creates a profound positive enhancement to a meal. Its cheerfulness and mental stimulation make a meal very desirable. Amber lighting is the most popular for evening. Its welcoming warmth adds a glowing ambiance to any room. **Amber** night lights emit a welcoming affect and aid in night vision. Amber is helpful for children who have intermittent sleep habits and awaken out of their sleep to go to the bathroom.

Green - Clear green light enhances a meal. Avoid yellow-green; it is very unappetizing. **Pale green** night lights are comforting and soothing. Pure green light gives a sense of safety, helps prevent nightmares and restless sleep patterns.

Blue - Blue lighting inhibits activity and gives a subdued atmosphere. It is suited for the family room for favorable and honest group discussions. Blue slows down the metabolic processes and gives food an unappetizing appearance. Consequently it is undesirable for dining. **Light blue** is ideal for the bedroom, since it creates a relaxing and peaceful atmosphere, and is especially beneficial for calming a hyperactive child. Dark blue has a cold appearance and is more suitable in warm weather.

Indigo - Indigo (black lighting) is too dark and hypnotic in effect for most surroundings. It is best suited for the bedroom, where its tranquil qualities provide a deep relaxing sleep and helps counteract insomnia.

Violet - Violet lighting is not harmonious for dining; however, it's ideal for the bedroom to promote a sound and restive sleep. Violet light (stained glass windows) is inspirational and stimulates dreaming, especially lucid dreams. **Magenta** light creates a playful and fun atmosphere for bedtime story telling and creative activities like playing musical instruments.

Rainbow/Full Spectrum - Natural sunlight provides the most beneficial effects for plants and all living things. It provides all the colors of the rainbow of natural light and is an excellent replacement for fluorescent lights, which can be harmful to the nervous system. Full spectrum lighting is a healthy choice..

CYBER SPACE

COLOR EFFECTS FROM COMPUTERS

The illumination of colors on the monitor screen of a computer are likened to the light waves of a dim light bulb. Gazing at the monitor is similar to starring at a traffic light. Specific colors emit certain wave lengths that affect the child's pituitary gland and general glandular system. Consider the color effects below as colors for text, background text and dominant colors on the monitor.

Red - Over stimulating to the eyes but invigorating to the muscles, staring at a red background, text or dominated color field on the monitor tires the eyes and agitates impulsive behavior.

Orange - Children find tangerine orange very appealing. Social and people-oriented orange will stimulate the appetite and need for relating to others.

Yellow - Black against yellow or amber is highly mentally simulative for short spurts of time and over powering to the brain for prolonged periods of time.

Green - Green is the most agreeable to the eyes and the entire body. Children are more responsive to lime green.

Blue - Blue against white is best for prolonged use.The deeper shades of blue are relaxing to the body and tension free to the eyes. A dark blue is expecially favorable for prolonged use on the computer.

Indigo - Against a white or cream background deep blue creates a sense of serious approach for working on computer projects. Over a prolonged period of time it is so mentally soothing that deep concentration is achieved only at small intervals. Indigo relaxes the body and stimulates a need to sleep or rest.

Violet - Bright purple or violet against a white background is stimulating to the imagination and helps develop creativity. Magenta as text and background is over stimulating and is best for short periods of visual exposure.

Neutrals - Black on white emits the least amount of UV Rays and is the sharpest contrast arrangement for the eyes to view over prolonged periods of time. This is a healthier color combination for the entire body.

RELATIONSHIPS

SPECTRUM IN BLUE

Blue is the color symbolic of heaven. It is timeless beauty in silence as the infinite sky, and gentleness in motion as a calm sea. Its universal appeal creates unity and harmony through its peaceful vibration. Add blue in your daily life for successful personal relationships.

FAMILY

Color can be used in various ways to improve family relationships - clothing, decorating, flowers and lighting. Improvise and discover other creative ways to use color for children and the family.

Red helps to motivate children to perform chores and invigorates them to participate in family sports and energetic activities. As an accent color to the family room, it enlivens family members and stimulates creative group activities. Too much red is over powering and can cause children to be hyperactive and quarrelsome. Do not dress aggressive and angry children in red. Dress children in red for others (babysitter/older siblings etc.) to pay attention to them.

Orange stimulates fun, laughter and congeniality among family members. Warm peach in the dining area creates a friendly atmosphere for lively family discussions at meal time. Add bright orange in the play/activity room for a warm, welcoming atmosphere for children to feel included.

Yellow sets a warm, cheerful, and friendly tone for family gatherings and for sick or recovering children. Lemon helps stimulate joyful interactions with family members. Golden yellow helps a group tackle a project with zest and see it through completion. It is influential in developing a brighter outlook for children. Too much yellow is over stimulating for preschoolers and causes irritability and frequent crying.

Green is the most commanding of colors. Green enables children to have total control over exercising their will-power in difficult situations. Its cooling and healing effects are non-threatening to others. Emerald green helps siblings work together toward mutual goals and support individual goals. Dress children in bright green to encourage sharing, caring and to balance them emotionally.

Blue is excellent for fair, peaceful and open family discussions. Deep blue promotes family unity, compromise, understanding and a sense of security. Its harmonious nature bonds family ties. Electric blue evokes a calm disposition and consideration toward siblings. Too much blue in a room can cause laziness and moodiness toward peers.

Indigo is ideal for truthful and confidential sharing. It is excellent for place settings at the dining table, to create a pleasant atmosphere and peaceful interaction among family members. Deep indigo bedroom accessories induce a calming sleep. Too much indigo can cause apathy and lethargy. Dress children in royal blue to relate harmoniously with family members.

Violet promotes spiritual strength and guidance from family elders. Add royal purple to a room for formal family gatherings. Bright purple and lavender, a favorite color among most young children, is best for a play/activity room to enhance creative activities (the arts) and imaginative exchanges between children.

CHILDREN

Red helps motivate physically lazy children to perform chores and to partake in family sports and festivities. Rose enhances creativity and productive, enjoyable activities. Pink is the color of daydreaming and fantasizing. Its soft sensation is great for creative play for the children's playroom. Children do not feel confined or limited in a pink environment.

Orange is an ideal color to bring a quiet, shy child out of his/her shell. Its friendly nature stimulates interaction among playmates and helps an inactive child become more involved. Orange also helps to promote sharing and polite social interaction among introverted children. Peach tones influence the qualities of graciousness and consideration toward others.

Yellow helps children develop memory retention and creates a positive attitude toward learning. Bright yellow is greatly enjoyed by younger children and helps them cope emotionally under negative circumstances. Yellow stimulates a conversation and brightens up their day!

Green creates a pleasant atmosphere where children can interact in a friendly helpful manner. Emerald green encourages strength in a frightening situation and enables them to heal from emotional and physical traumas. Its influence can help children develop self-esteem and adaptability. Children are very attracted to neon/flourescent, glowing lime green, which excites their creative imagination and ability to fantasize with peers.

Blue (vivid) has a calming effect upon the emotions and physical activities of children. The physically relaxing quality of blue helps to settle down hyperactive children. It promotes sharing, relating and the ability to understand another's viewpoint. Blue influences children to listen, to speak softly and to get along with peers. A dominant blue room creates a cool atmosphere which can help inhibit temper tantrums and violent emotions.

Indigo in a bedroom helps to inhibit nightmares, restless sleep and sleepwalking. Deep indigo is tranquilizing for nervous and emotionally upset children. This is not a favorite color for most children. It is preferred by the religious or spiritually educated children. Deep indigo helps develop a conscience, sound judgment and good manners.

Violet stimulates a children's rich and expansive imagination and helps to develop an appreciation for the arts and culture. Warm tints of lavender are great for a progressive education that enhances the children's creativity and natural talents.

FRIENDSHIP

Red stimulates the spirit of activity in physical sports. It can challenge a friendship through competitive games and fun activities. Red can be both intimidating and invigorating. Rose stimulates creative play among children. Pink expresses affection and gentle interaction among playmates.

Orange is the most vibrant color for a playful adventurous day and the most fun color for a celebration. Bright orange opens up children's hearts to share with others and excites their humorous side. Peach expresses genuine friendship. Salmon and coral cements a friendship with affection.

Yellow evokes a lively conversation and carefree interaction among children. Yellow uplifts their spirits and motivates intellectual activities, such as word games that challenge their memory. Lemon yellow expresses thoughtfulness toward others. Yellow flowers will cheer up a sad or sick friend.

Green expresses self-assurance in awkward situations with peers. It will help children feel comfortable in approaching others for assistance. When visiting a sick friend wearing emerald is pleasant and healing. Lime green is festive for parties and outdoor games with peers. Green is commanding in peer teaching.

Blue is the best color for behaving civil with peers. Deep blue is great for relaxing, exchanging ideas and for developing a special friendship.

Indigo expresses caring and understanding among friends. Royal blue helps give a friend moral support in a difficult situation. It expresses sincerity, honesty and brotherly love.

Violet inspires creative talents that are shared with peers - art, music, dance and drama. Purple /magenta stimulates the imagination during playtime with peers- imaginary playmates, story telling and making unique handmade creations.

PETS

Even though most animals do not perceive color as color they do sense the vibrations of color. The color of the animals accessories- color dishes, bedding and toys can influence the animal's behavior.

Red - stimulates activity for an older animal. It creates hyperactivity for young or healthy pets. Rose is preferred to adorn a pet with affection. Pink is great for loving interaction among children and pets. It appeals to the animal's gentle nature and tones down the aggressive nature.

Orange - Pets will eat more and quicker in a bright orange space. Peach tones are more enhancing and warming to the personality of the animal. It will help make a shy pet more friendly and stimulate interaction among other animals.

Yellow - Yellow is the best color to use while training a pet. It is excellent for a pet that never goes outdoors; it brings the warm, glowing, sunshine effect indoors.

Green - Grass green and bright green tones give the appearance of the outdoors in a pet's room. It can feel

64

refreshing and always seem clean and sterile. Green can normalize and stabilize the health and physical activities of the animal.

Blue - Blue has a great calming effect upon a traumatized animal. It will also promote harmony among pets and family members. The deeper shades of blue have a tranquilizing effect on animals. It will help slow down an overly aggressive pet.

Indigo - Bright indigo is best suited to lesson hyperactivity and calm an injured pet. Royal blue and deep indigo promote more sleep or rest and help the pet recover from sickness or an operation.

Violet - Lavender is favored for the adornment of most animals. Its androgynous quality and beauteous nature is appealing. The deep violet is best used as a surrounding color or bedding for new pets, especially puppies, kittens, etc. It helps them feel more comfortable with the unfamiliar new home. They will have a more restful sleep and won't cry as much. Violet can also aid in teaching animals word commands.

Learning Techniques

SPECTRUM IN INDIGO

Indigo is the color of the night sky, the reflection of timelessness- the essence of space. It is symbolic of the balancing scales of life, creating order and harmony within the universe. As a force of pure ideal love, its vibration links all humanity as one. Its gentle effects upon your daily life create trust, understanding, and affection toward others.

Our informational and technological society is advancing so rapidly that our children need learning techniques that are simple and effective. Nearly one hundred years ago eight-year-old children could name only four colors and today a three year old can do the same. Color can play a part in helping the child to learn more efficiently and expediently.

Color association is especially beneficial for cognition and remembrance. Colored objects have a greater cue to memory than uncolored ones. Studies conducted in the field of neuropsychology have proven that colors represent particular sensations and specific associations with objects that the child is familiar with. For example, several different objects of the same color such as a pale blue - piece of paper, a pillow, or a bike - would be suggestive to the brain of a sky or water. The color from earlier conditioning reminds the child of something it represents.

EDUCATING THE RIGHT BRAIN WITH COLOR

A simple method for recalling words or remembering spelling is to use different colors for each letter of a word. It is best to begin with green (go) for the first letter and red (stop) for the last letter. Green implies to go or begin and red to stop or end. After the children begin with green, the sequence of the rainbow is the most effective color combination to use. For example, the word LEARN - L is green, E is blue, A is indigo, R is violet and N is red. Children love rainbows. Using the rainbow for cognition and color association makes learning enjoyable and successful for the children.

Another method of color association is mind mapping, which is used for outlining information about a subject. Children are given a rainbow assortment of color markers and asked to draw the shape of a radiating sun in the center of the page. For example, if the subject they are learning is ecology they are instructed to choose their favorite color and write the word ecology in the center of the sun. Next the children select a different color for each theme for ecology. Writing out from the center like the shape of a radiating sun they list the different themes of the subject. One of each color is used to associate with a particular theme. The children will be able to remember and comprehend the subject matter through the use of color association.

COLOR THERAPY GLASSES AND COLOR COVERS FOR READING AND LEARNING

One way to incorporate color as a tool for improving learning when reading or performing a task is through the use of Color Therapy glasses and transparent colored acetate overlays. Color can have physical, emotional and cognitive effects on the child's behavior and on the ability to concentrate and focus on a particular task or reading assignment. Color overlays are easy to use and are designed only for placing over reading material. The color application for Color Therapy glasses also pertains to the use of color overlays. They can be used during the entire reading lesson as long as breaks from using the overlays are included. For example red so packed with energy that it is best to take one minute breaks every 5-10 minutes. It is strongly recommended not to use a red overlay more than 30 consecutive minutes per day. The positive effects of red are immediate.

Along with these color techniques it is best to have the child involved in the process of color exploration for successful learning. A rainbow assortment of mats or construction paper can be placed on the desk or near the study area. At the beginning of each session the child can choose the color of the day. The child is given a choice in order to be motivated to participate and to promote self-control and interest. This collaborative process doesn't isolate or overburden the child. The child will look forward to future sessions and become more cooperative and responsive to the goals at hand. Experiment with color overlays and/or Color Therapy glasses until the particular goal is achieved.

HOW TO USE COLOR THERAPY GLASSES

The colors below are recommended for a specific purpose. Select one color for a particular result. Monitor the child to assess the effects of the color chosen. Eventually children can select a color they prefer for the day. Thirty minutes for one session is the maximum amount of time and one minute the minimum time limit that children need to expose their eyes to a certain color, while reading or performing a task. Results for each color should be recorded. Results are immediate. If one color doesn't work select another.

APPLICATION OF COLOR THERAPY GLASSES

Red - Involvement, action, courage to go forward. Excellent at the beginning of a reading lesson or task for motivation and to energize the child. Duration: Alternate between a 5-10 minute reading session and a one minute break.

Pink - weakens an aggressive attitude and strengthens a feeling of acceptance. It is easier on the eyes than red. Duration: 15 - 30 minutes. (Only available as an overlay)

Orange - Ability to share with others and promotes friendliness. Best for cooperation in group activities. Duration: 10 - 20 minutes.

Yellow - Retain information, develop a positive attitude. Most effective for memorization and recalling knowledge. Yellow is the most difficult color to focus on for a long period of time. Duration: Alternate between reading and a one minute break for 10- 20 minute intervals.

Green - Attention, responsive, a neutralizer- good for any need. Yellow-green is best to counteract the negative effects of fluorescent lighting and reading in harsh sunlight. Green is easiest on the eyes. Duration: 15 -30 minutes

Blue - Compliance, compromise, conformity, and tension-free. Light blue is soothing to the eyes and very calming for a hyperactive child. Duration: 15 - 30 minute intervals.

Indigo - is conscientiousness, concentration, calmness. The strongest color to tranquilize a nervous child. Duration: 1-3 minutes. (Use indigo only with Color Therapy glasses).

Violet - is Imagination, problem-solving, inspiration, and creativity. Duration several minutes. **Magenta** - Excellent for creative motivation, original thinking, and playfulness. Duration: 15 - 30 minutes.

BODY AND MIND LEARNING METHODS

Children learn best when they involve several of their senses during the learning process. Color therapy involves the use of all the senses. Aroma therapy is one of the important elements of color therapy. Each scent vibrates a specific color and each color a particular vibration. Color association and scent is excellent for recollection and retention of information and readiness to learn.

Art applied to the learning process is very effective for acquiring knowledge. For example finger paints incorporate several senses and combine both right and left brain processes that enhance cognition. Through the process of creating visual art children use both their mind and body, which is beneficial for learning words, solving math problems, memorization, and expanding creative imagination.

Music is a very powerful tool that creates a positive atmosphere and influences the mind and body for learning. Musical notes each resonate to a particular wavelength that corresponds to a color. For example, the rhythm of 17th century Baroque music is one beat per second. As children listen to this classical music the heart can begin to synchronize with one beat per second. This particular music is known to relax the body and alert the brain, which can be a perfect combination for learning. The classical Baroque music of Bach, Vivaldi, or Handel played during lessons can effect a positive change in the children's readiness and concentration to learn. This is excellent background music when reciting information to the children. It will enhance learning and the memory process. Instructing with a varied tone of voice can accelerate or vary results.

COLOR BREATHING

Thinking and breathing a certain color has an effect on the body and mind. Breathing techniques in meditation have proven to energize the mind and relax the body. Each color has a specific purpose for the children's learning process.

A specific color is selected for a special purpose. Each color breathing exercise is more successful if the following technique is used. For example, the mind is able to focus on one idea through using the color yellow. The breath is held a few seconds in between inhaling and exhaling the color.

Example of breathing color- Breathing yellow is best before a creative learning exercise or before an introduction to a new subject. Instruct the children to visualize breathing in the color yellow to a count of two in between inhaling and exhaling for just three to seven times. This brief exercise should be used according to the ages of the children. Longer segments for older children and shorter ones for young children are recommended.

Breathing **red** is excellent before physical activities that require a lot of energy, such as physical education.

Breathing **orange** enables socialization and cooperative interaction with groups.

Breathing **yellow** enhances memorization and concentration.

Breathing **green** enables preparation, focused listening and proper attention to instruction.

Breathing **blue** aids in relaxation, emotional calm and harmonious interaction in group activities.

Breathing **Indigo** calms the nerves (before a stressful exam) and tranquilizes the mind and body (after competitive sports).

Breathing **violet** excites the creative imagination and self-expression. This is the best color for creativity with the arts; music, dance, visual art and theater.

LEARNING WITH ALL THE SENSES

. **RED**

Sound/Music Therapy - Red is the musical note of C. High pitched sounds and lively dynamic music vibrate the color red. It stimulates the nervous system and the muscular system. The sound is so powerful that children are urged to dance or to engage in vigorous activity. Red promotes the release of energy to combat stress.

Touch - Red is the sensation of heat. It is hot as a flaming fire or dry as the hot desert sand. Intense red is like a melting metal rod of extreme heat.

Taste - Red is pungent and found in stimulating spices, especially hot ones such as cayenne pepper and cinnamon. It stimulates circulation, digestion, and mental alertness. In excess it can cause irritability, over eating and dehydration.

Visual -Tantalizing and sensational, red flirts with the eyes. Alarming and alerting in its impact, it impels the viewer to look at it and take particular notice. Pinks and rose shades beckon children to enjoyment and affection. The lighter shades are suggestive of youthfulness and babyhood. The deep tones of red are reminiscent of blood and subdues vitality. Red puts the entire system on alert.

Scent/Aroma Therapy - The fragrances of red are patchouli (rose pink), sandal-wood (deep red), geranium (bright red), rose and jasmine.

Form/Art Therapy - Shape: the square relates to red.
Line: the vertical line expresses the feeling nature of red.

ORANGE

Sound/Music Therapy - Orange is the musical note of D. It is expressed through a heavy rhythmic beat, loud to harsh tones and lively tempo, such as rock'n roll, hard rock, and heavy metal music (stomach pump music). These vibrations affect the stomach. It is stimulating and lively. The effects of these vibrations are great for vigorous body movements and fast dancing. Orange music is designed for physical expression.

Touch - Orange is warm as the rays of the sun, or hot as bursting sparks of fire.

Taste - Orange is sour in taste, as found in oranges, yogurt, and acidic fruits. It helps eliminate excess gas, sharpens the senses, and stimulates circulation and digestion. Orange promotes strength, vitality and firmness to the tissues of the skin. In excess, it can putrefy the blood system, cause a burning sensation and hyperacidity.The spice saffron is bright yellow-orange and stimulates stomach secretions.

Visual - Brilliant as the sun to the eyes, orange activates the appetite and stimulates the palate. It is jovial, forceful and emanates vitalizing energy. It invokes the senses of physical pleasures and sociability. The brighter tones are somewhat harsh to the eye. The lighter tones and tints are exceptionally pleasing to the senses.

Scent/Aroma Therapy - The fragrances of orange are vanilla and almond.

Form/Art Therapy - Shape: the rectangle relates to orange.
Line: the diagonal line expresses the feeling nature of orange.

YELLOW

Sound/Music Therapy - Yellow is the musical note of E. Its cheerful, uplifting music, allows children to experience positive feelings. Happy tunes that make children sing and nostalgic melodies stimulate the memory of positive past experiences. Yellow puts a warm smile on children's faces and puts them in a good mood.

Touch - Yellow feels warm as a ray of golden sunshine.

Taste - Yellow tastes salty. It is found in stimulating spices like turmeric, seaweed, and sea salt. It can stimulate your digestion and in greater amounts acts as a laxative. It promotes tissue growth and balances the minerals of the body through retention of water, and relieves muscle stiffness. If used in excess, it can cause an imbalance in the blood and cause vomiting.

Visual - Yellow is brighter than white. It jumps out at the viewer. Children cannot avoid its loud personality. It stimulates the mind to focus and remember words and numbers (note the yellow notepad's popularity and use). It will attract children and bring attention to itself. Yellow beckons children to think before they act. It is the most difficult color to look at for any length of time.

Scent/Aroma Therapy - Yellow fragrances are iris, clove and rattan.

Form/Art Therapy - Shape: the triangle relates to yellow.
Line: the jagged line expresses the feeling nature of yellow.

GREEN

Sound/Music Therapy - According to Isaac Newton, the musical note of F is green. Like a breath of spring air, its melody is serene and healing to all of the senses. Pleasant, relaxing harmonies and light, lively rhythms in perfect balance resound to green vibrations.

Touch - Cooling to the touch, green appears to feel moist or misty. The darker shades and muted tones feel damp. The brighter and more vivid tones feel like morning dew.

Taste - Green's astringent quality is found in unripe bananas, herbs like witch hazel, and aloe vera, and vegetables such as beans and cabbages. It promotes healing of the skin, firms the tissues, provides a mineral supplement, and strengthens mucous membranes. In excessive amounts, it can cause muscle spasms and circulatory problems.

Visual - Most soothing to the eyes, green suggests coolness in warm weather and warmth in cool weather. It is restful and pleasant to the body. It gives the feeling of hope, and evokes a sense of well-being.

Scent/Aroma Therapy - The fragrances of green are musk and spring rain.

Form/Art Therapy - Shape: the hexagon relates to green. Line: the check mark expresses the feeling nature of green.

BLUE

Sound/Music Therapy - Blue is the musical note of G. Soft and slow melodic music vibrates the color blue. Its effects are soothing, dreamy, and relaxing. Blue evokes thoughts and deep emotions. It is very healing in effect, by slowing down the heart rate and calming the nervous system.

Touch - Blue is soft as a cloud and transparent and smooth as a wave in water. Its sensation is moistness.

Taste - Blue is very sweet, as found in sugars and sweet herbs. It promotes growth, contentment, and strength. In excess, it can lead to overweight and inhibit digestion.

Visual - Blue is the most pleasing color for the eyes to perceive. It is a favorite color choice among all ages, especially bright blue for babies. Blue is cool, peaceful and tranquil to the eyes.

Scent/Aroma Therapy - The fragrances of blue are magnolia and orange flower.

Form /Art Therapy- Shape: the circle relates to blue.
Line: the horizontal line express the feeling nature of blue.

INDIGO

Sound/Music Therapy - Indigo is the musical note of A. Its melody is emotionally soothing and spiritually moving. Classical, religious hymns, and sentimental love songs resound the color indigo. This musical hue opens the heart, mind, and soul. Its deeply felt message has universal appeal and is understood and enjoyed by all cultures and religions. These melodies can move children's hearts to tears of joy and love.

Touch - Indigo has the appearance of extreme coldness, like the crystalline ice of outer space.

Taste - Indigo is balanced between sweet and bitter. It is a normalizer of taste. It is almost tasteless. Indigo vegetables are rich in vitamin K and improve eyesight and inner sight. Indigo acts as a sedative and improves nervous ailments. In excess amounts it inhibits reasoning ability and proper visual judgment.

Visual - Indigo is deeply soothing and peaceful to the mind. It appeals to children's logical reasoning ability and intellect. Hypnotic in effect, indigo triggers vivid memories from their past, possibly even past lifetimes. It is the ideal hue for deep, relaxing sleep and inner tranquillity.

Scent/Aroma Therapy - The fragrances of indigo are cinnamon and lavender.

Form/Art Therapy - Shape: the crescent relates to indigo.
Line: the wavy line expresses the feeling nature of indigo.

VIOLET

Sound/ Music Therapy- Violet is the musical note of B. Dreamy and euphoric, this melodic tone leads children into the world of enchantment and magic. It is so heavenly that an altered state of consciousness might be experienced. Its hypnotic vibrations are completely calming. Religious music like the Gregorian Chant is this mystical and magical hue.

Touch - Violet is cooling or warmly mystical. The light tints feel magically soft and the dark hue incredibly ethereal, seemingly from another dimension. It's the visionary spark of creativity.

Taste - Violet is bitter-tasting. Bitter purple herbs, vegetables and fruits are the best for killing germs, for detoxification of the body and purification of the blood system. The worst tastes help weight loss and promote cleansing and mental functioning. Consumed in excess, it can induce nervousness, irritability, insomnia and too much weight loss.

Visual - Violet is soothing and calming to the mind, it stimulates the imagination and induces sleep or deep relaxation. The warmer tones with red hues are more vitalizing and charming and evoke keen insight (inner perception), sensitivity and fantasy. Magenta and warm purples are the tones of aesthetic beauty and are best used in creative environments.

Scent/Aroma Therapy - The fragrances of violet are clove, mint and peppermint.

Form/Art Therapy - Shape: the oval relates to violet.
Line: the curved line expresses the feeling nature of violet.

DRAWING EXERCISES

Since ancient civilization through modern times, humankind has utilized symbols to express itself. Symbols are a universal language which conveys specific meanings. One shape can evoke a deep response and express many words.

Red - Through the process of creating a square, which expresses the specific color red, children can experience the feeling and energy of that color.They can draw or doodle a square on paper, inscribe it in the sand, or in mid-air. Making a square will help empower them to achieve the following:
1. to become courageous and to overcome fears;
2. to become motivated;
3. to become grounded and feel secure in a relationship or situation;
4. to begin a physical task.

Orange - Through the process of creating a rectangle, which expresses the specific color **orange**, children can experience the feeling and energy of that color. Children can draw or doodle a rectangle on paper, inscribe it in the sand, or in mid-air. Making a rectangle will help empower them to achieve the following:
1. to become more sociable;
2. to create positive changes;
3. to increase intellectual confidence;
4. to win a debate or contest.

Yellow - Through the process of creating a triangle, which expresses the specific color **yellow**, children can experience the feeling and energy of that color. Children can draw or doodle a triangle on paper, inscribe it in the sand, or in mid-air. Making a triangle will help empower them to achieve the following:
1. to prepare for positive action;
2. to develop memory retention and intellectual learning;
3. to strengthen the mind;
4. to become happy and joyful.

Green - Through the process of creating a hexagon, which expresses the specific color green, children can experience the feeling and energy of that color. Children can draw or doodle a hexagon on paper, inscribe it in the sand, or in mid-air. Making a hexagon will help empower them to achieve the following:
1. to heal and balance the mind, body, and spirit;
2. to become comfortable;
3. to begin a new project and exercise their will-power;
4. to focus on learning instruction.

Blue - Through the process of creating a circle, which expresses the specific color blue, children can experience the feeling and energy of that color. Children can draw or doodle a circle on paper, inscribe it in the sand, or in mid-air. Making a circle will help empower them to achieve the following:
1. to relax the body and calm the emotions;
2. to reach a solution to a problem;
3. to become patient in an overbearing situation;
4. to maintain spiritual development.

Indigo - Through the process of creating a crescent, which expresses the specific color indigo, children can experience the feeling and energy of that color. Children can draw or doodle a crescent on paper, inscribe it in the sand, or in mid-air. Making a crescent will help empower them to achieve the following:
1. to create harmony between thoughts and emotions;
2. to become receptive to others;
3. to develop spiritual understanding;
4. to become deeply relaxed.

Violet - Through the process of creating an oval, which expresses the specific color violet, children can experience the feeling and energy of that color. Children can draw or doodle an oval on paper, inscribe it in the sand, or in mid-air. Making an oval will help empower children to achieve the following:
1. to develop intuition;
2. to stimulate creativity;
3. to develop individuality;
4. to express the ability to play.

COLOR INDEX FOR BEHAVIOR MODIFICATION

The powerful unconscious and subliminal messages that colors give can help improve and influence behavioral changes for children. This color index was compiled to provide a specific color that would either inhibit a negative behavior or enhance a positive one.

There are a number of ways that color therapy can be incorporated daily into children's lives. Colors children wear, visualize, eat, imagine, touch and that involve all of the senses are most effective. For example, to increase children's appetite and to help them become more pleasantly social dress them in orange, use an orange table cloth or orange place settings at mealtime, bathe them in an orange bath, have them imagine a large orange as big as the room, wear orange Color Therapy glasses for 10-15 minutes, place an orange mat at their classroom desk and decorate their personal space with bright orange as an accent. Experiment-ation, repetition and creative use of color will give the best results. Use your own creative imagination, keep a record of results and have fun with the colorful responses.

COLOR TO ENCOURAGE POSITIVE BEHAVIOR

Achiever - Red
Adventurous - Red
Affectionate - Pink
Altruistic - Magenta
Athletic - Red
Assertive- Red
Brave - Red
Calm - Blue
Carefree - Orange
Charming - Magenta
Cheerful - Yellow
Commanding - Green
Committed - Indigo
Communicative - Blue
Compromise - Blue
Confidence - Red
Compliance - Blue
Conscientious - Indigo
Considerate - Orange
Content - Blue
Constructive - Green
Courage - Red
Creative - Violet
Decisiveness - Indigo
Determination- Red
Devoted - Indigo
Diplomacy - Peach
Dynamic- Red
Energetic - Red
Enthusiasm - Orange
Friendly - Orange
Generous - Green
Gentle - Pink
Gregarious - Orange
Helpful - Orange
Honest - Indigo
Humanitarian - Magenta
Idealistic- Violet
Imaginative - Violet
Industrious - Yellow
Innovative - Yellow
Inquisitive- Yellow
Inspirational - Violet
Intellectual - Yellow
Interactive - Orange

Intuitive - Violet
Investigative - Yellow
Joyful - Yellow
Kindness - Orange
Leadership- Red
Logical - Yellow
Loyal - Indigo
Loving - Pink
Mental motivation - Yellow
Motivation- Orange
Optimistic - Yellow
Original - Violet
Organized- Yellow
Outgoing - Orange
Patient - Blue
Peaceful - Blue
Personable - Orange
Physical energy - Red
Physical strength - Red
Persuasive - Blue
Pleasant - Green
Practical- Green
Precognition - Violet
Progressive - Yellow
Reliable - Green
Responsive - Green
Satisfaction - Blue
Self-assured - Red
Self-confidence - Red
Self-moderation - Blue
Self motivated - Red
Self-reliant- Blue
Self-respect - Green
Sensitive - Violet
Serene - Blue
Serious - Indigo
Sharing - Orange
Sincere - Peach
Social - Orange
Stamina - Red
Studious - Yellow
Spiritual -Violet
Spontaneous- Red
Thoughtful- Indigo
Trustworthy - Indigo

COLOR TO HELP MODIFY NEGATIVE BEHAVIOR

Abrasive - Orange
Aggressive - Deep Blue
Agitated - Blue
Angry - Deep Blue
Anti-social - Peach
Anxious - Blue
Argumentative - Blue
Arrogant - Green
Authoritative - Blue
Boisterous - Green
Bossy - Blue
Cautious - Orange
Collector - Yellow
Complaining -Green
Conceited - Blue
Cowardice - Red
Critical - Indigo
Cruel - Peach
Cynical - Yellow
Day dreamer - Yellow
Deceitful - Indigo
Defiant - Blue
Depressed - Yellow
Disorderly - Yellow
Disquiet -Blue
Distrustful - Yellow
Easily hurt - Pink
Emancipation - Green
Envious - Orange
Exorbitant - Green
Fanatical - Green
Fatigued - Red
Fear of loss - Yellow
Fear of rejection - Yellow
Feel cheated - Green
Fickle - Indigo
Finicky - Green
Fussy - Yellow
Grief stricken - Green
Gruff - Orange
Glutinous - Indigo
Hyperactive - Deep Blue
Impatient - Blue
Impulsive - Green
Inferiority - Bright Blue

Inflexible - Green
Intolerant - Indigo
Instigator - Green
Irritable - Blue
Jealous - Yellow
Judgmental - Indigo
Lazy - Red
Low appetite - Orange
Low self-esteem - Yellow
Misunderstood - Indigo
Moody - Green
Narrow-minded - Violet
Nervous - Indigo
Obnoxious - Blue
Obsessed - Yellow
Obstinate - Yellow
Overconfident - Green
Oversensitive - Blue
Passive - Red
Pessimistic - Yellow
Pompous - Blue
Pouts - Yellow
Quick to take offense - Blue
Rage - Blue
Reckless - Deep Blue
Reproachful - Blue
Repugnant - Indigo
Restless - Indigo
Secretive - Orange
Selfish - Green
Self- pity - Orange
Shy - Orange
Sly naiveté - Violet
Stubborn - Orange
Sulky - Yellow
Tired - Red
Troublesome - Yellow
Unfair - Blue
Unrealistic - Yellow
Uncontrollable - Green
Vain - Green
Violent - Pink
Whiny - Blue
Withdrawn - Bright Blue
Worrisome - Green

PHYSICAL, MENTAL AND SPIRITUAL WELL BEING

SPECTRUM IN VIOLET

Violet is the inspirational color of the artist, the mystic and the most refined in character. Its majestic and spiritual power symbolizes nobility and royalty. It is the essence of patience progressing through time. The daily use of violet can create intuitive and sensitive understanding in all your affairs.

PHYSICAL HEALTH

There are seven major colors of the rainbow, seven major notes of a scale of music and there are also seven major energy fields in the human body. The body functions like a computerized storage battery. There are points of energy where vibrations are absorbed into the system, stored, saved and released. Their degree of functioning is greatly determined by the way children live their lives and how they express themselves. Inability to cope with certain aspects of life will usually manifest as physical symptoms in a specific area of the body. However, children's energy fields can be tuned into greater balance through the positive and correct use of color.

As an adjunct with other remedies color can be used to help improve children's particular physical conditions in various ways; through a color diet, wearing Color Therapy glasses, specific color clothing- a blanket and/or scarf, administering color lighting, color breathing, color meditation, etc.

HOW COLOR THERAPY GLASSES WORK

Color Therapy glasses allow light to become the specific color of the glasses. This colored light then enters the retina. The colored light wave stimulates the pituitary gland, which influences the glandular system and the endocrine system, which can cause a chain reaction to occur throughout the body. Many people have experienced that wearing the red Color Therapy glasses for a few minutes or less can help to relieve a headache. For another example others have been shown that by wearing the indigo Color Therapy glasses the viewer may see an aura.

The color information below applies to the use of all color applications and is intended to be used as a supplement for specific physical states.

Red stimulates the body in a constructive manner. It may help to stop hemorrhages and the production of red blood cells. It is a vital vibration to help increase physical strength for the entire body and to help stimulate the will-power to live!

Scarlet is a brain and arterial stimulant and can help reduce inflammation. It is a kidney energizer and boosts the morale. It increases vitality and courage. It is a beneficial vibration in general throughout the body.

Pink affects the mind more than the body. It helps to raise the vibrations of the body and can help to promote rejuvenation.

Orange is a body normalizer and can be beneficial for asthma, respiratory disorders, cramps, stomach aches and spasms. It can help to improve indigestion, ulcers and the thyroid. It replenishes depleted enthusiasm and vitality.

Yellow is a great laxative. It can help to increase the flow of bile, stomach and intestinal activity. Applied outside the body, it can help to reduce swelling. It is a powerful stimulant to the nervous system.

Lemon can help to relieve a cold and flu symptoms and can help to build the bones.

Green with its regenerative and balancing qualities, is the master beneficiary, especially the emerald and bluish hues. It can assist in dissolving blood clots, help to build the muscles, tissues and skin and can help break up congestion. It helps eliminate germs, viruses, and toxic wastes. It can gently bring restoration and balance to the entire body.

Blue is used to help fevers, and to normalize a fast pulse rate, blue also can act as a pulmonary sedative, help depress the motor nerves, and may aide in combating infection. It encourages relaxation, and may help subdue physical and mental disorders. Blue can be beneficial for sore throats, laryngitis, hoarseness, dysentery, jaundice, cuts, burns and bruises.

Indigo can help to purify the blood stream and may be beneficial for acute bronchitis, convulsions, nervous ailments, lung and nasal disturbances and tonsillitis. As a sedative it can be helpful for hemorrhages and internal bleeding. As an astringent it can be useful for tightening and toning the muscles, nerves and skin.

Violet may help bladder trouble, concussions, epilepsy, kidney ailments, neuralgia, nervous and mental disorders, rheumatism, sciatica, scalp and skin disorders. It helps to induce a deep, relaxed sleep and may help to maintain the potassium-sodium balance in the body.

Magenta can be helpful for heart disorders, kidneys, and emotional balance. It can act as a diuretic and may help to normalize the blood pressure.

FOOD AND NUTRITION

A rainbow selection of solarized living foods- fruits and vegetables are essential to a daily diet for whole health.

Red fruits and vegetables are enriched with iron, copper, and B vitamins to increase vitality. Most red foods are delectable, appealing and tantalize the taste buds as well as excite the appetite.

Orange fruits and vegetables are rich in vitamin B. Orange table linen and tableware, as well as surroundings, increase the appetite and stimulate excessive eating.

Yellow foods are highly solarized by the sunlight. Yellow fruits and vegetables provide vitamins A and C to balance energy. Enriched with nature's energy source, solarized foods increase mental alertness and give a radiant glow to the body.

Green vegetables and fruits are enriched with vitamin C and rich minerals. The more saturated and brighter the green, the more nutritional value in the content of the food. Green garnishments (parsley) and accessories (napkins, tablecloth) add in creating a wholesome appetite and natural environment for dining.

Blue is an excellent background to display foods harmoniously and pleasingly. It slows down the metabolism and visually enhances the taste of a meal.

Indigo fruits and eggplant contain vitamin K. Indigo is an excellent background color to display foods harmoniously and creatively.

Violet fruits and vegetables are enriched with vitamin D. Grapes, plums, elderberry and purple cabbage are some of nature's delicious and nutritious purple pleasures.

PHYSICAL EXERCISE

The colors children wear and visualize can influence their performance and be beneficial for physical activities. Select the best colors for the particular goal.

Red is competitive in nature and enables children to react quickly in an unanticipated situation. It alerts the body to rapid action. It is the best color to use for competition and to instill the will to win in an individual or a group. It is excellent for all sports and activities where speed, endurance and physical strength are essential for optimum results. Red is great to help children shed those unwanted pounds and give them the energy to engage in fast dancing, exercising and daring sports. Paint their physical appetite red!

Orange will give children the confidence to do difficult or silly routines in a group. It will provide them with a happy disposition toward their exercise program. Orange is great for group activities where everyone must participate equally. It enhances teamwork and friendship. Orange signifies glory and promotes the confidence to be victorious in competitive sports, as well as an enthusiastic spectator.

Yellow is great for activities and all forms of aerobic exercise where fast movement and dance steps, or memorized segments of a routine are needed. It is ideal for gymnastics, example floor-exercise. All record keeping of physical attainments are best kept on yellow paper. Mount the child's ideal weight picture on a yellow background and instruct them to think positive when viewing the picture!

Green's cooling properties and balancing nature promote health maintenance. Green will allow maximum performance for children without harm or damage to a weak area of the body. The emerald, aqua and turquoise tones give an exhilerating feeling to the body and instills a hopeful attitude for progress. Use green for a balanced physical routine.

Blue is excellent for weight gain and building muscles. It helps children maintain a slow and steady pace for all physical activity. It is especially wonderful for yoga exercises where breathing and movement are synchronized for mental and physical balancing.

Indigo is most beneficial for the cool-down exercises after working out strenuously. It is perfect for sedate and mental exercises requiring slow movement and concentration. It helps tone muscles and calm nerves. It is best used for most water sports and physical activities that require common sense and calm thinking to avoid injury to the participant. It gives the mental readiness to partake in risky sports where proper and safe responses, not emotional reactions, are required.

Violet has a sedative effect. It is best utilized for the last performance of a dance routine or any type of physical activity needing aesthetic appeal. Since it will stimulate the imagination, it is best for boring physical and monotonous routines, where the mind can safely wander. It is excellent for isometrics and slow, deliberate movements such as Tai Chi. It is ideal for posture and yoga meditation.

COLOR AND LIGHT THERAPY

The action of light on a living being is photochemical and referred to as photo biology. As a major sensory organ of the body the skin absorbs visible light, which causes biological reactions in the body. The light wave of a specific color stimulates the pituitary gland, which influences the glandular and endocrine system and causes a chain of reactions that occur throughout the body.

White sunlight contains all the colors of the rainbow and provides the full benefit of every color in equal amounts simultaneously. This powerful healing life-force is essential for the total health of all living things. Even the smallest amount of light is uplifting to the spirit and revitalizing to the physical body. Moderate exposure to sunlight promotes a happier disposition and healthier skin.

APPLICATION OF COLOR THERAPY

The recipient of color therapy needs to lie down or sit with the back straight. For best results with color, lights need to penetrate the exposed skin of the entire body. If this is uncomfortable for the child use a cotton, wool, silk or any other natural material to cover over the entire body except for the head. Place the light above the head if the child is sitting, or above the center of the body if the child is in a reclining position. Choose 3 different colored lights, one for each procedure. Perform each step for just a few minutes or as long as one song. The entire session may last a short time, 5 - 10 minutes or a half hour depending on the child. Experiment and make it an enjoyable experience.

TO INDUCE PHYSICAL STIMULATION AND MOTIVATION

Warm colors tends to stimulate muscular activity. Red light acts as a stimulant that is followed by a sense of depression. Cool hues relax the muscles. Blue light relaxes and is followed by an enlivened response. In color light therapy the timing of the application of colored light and the color sequence is crucial to a given response.

1. **Stimulation** - Warm lights: red, orange, amber, or peach- a bright illumination with loud music.

2. **Relaxation** - Cool lights: blue, green, or violet, a dimmer illumination and no music or soft and soothing music.

3. **Neutral** (balancing)- Yellow and yellowish green light.

TO INDUCE STIMULATION FOR ASSERTIVE BEHAVIOR

1.**Stimulation** - Begin with lively tolerable loud music and warm colors, preferably red with bright illumination for several minutes.

2.**Relaxation** - Immediately follow with exposure to cool colors, preferably blue with dimmer illumination and no music.

3. **Neutral (balancing)-** End with soothing music and expose the child to a pale yellow or white bright illumination.

TO INDUCE RELAXATION FOR PASSIVE BEHAVIOR

1. **Stimulation** - Start with soothing music or no music and several minutes exposure to cool colors, preferably blue with dim illumination.

2. **Relaxation** - Immediately follow with exposure to warm colors, preferably red and bright illumination.

3. **Neutral** (balancing) - End with exposure to pale yellow or bright white light.

RAINBOW BATHING

Rainbow bathing for children is a fun experience with many benefits. The blend of color which is an energy, and water- a conductor of energy- equals a powerful combination for well-being. Coloring the bath water a specific color can evoke an energy which will enhance a desired need. Mix either colored bubble bath, food coloring or Rainbow Bathing minerals into the bath water.

Red - Vitality, Physical Energy. Associated with heat, red is the most revitalizing color bath and best for mid day bathing or early morning bathing. Red is excellent for a child that has muscular inhibition and/or for recovering from a cold or the flu. It is also good for physical therapy, to stimulate life energy for the muscles and energize the entire physical system.

Pink - Affection, Physically Gentle. Excellent for any time of day and especially for a young child. Pink is pampering to all of the senses and helps an ill child recover through tender loving vibrations.

Orange - Appetite Increase, Sociability, Friendly Disposition. Morning and mid day bath. Stimulates positive emotions and strengthens a healthy appetite. Orange helps to enliven all the senses and decrease inhibitions.

Yellow - Self-esteem, Joy, Mental Clarity. Morning or mid day bath. Provides mental stimulation and increase interest and curiosity.

89

Green - Self Control, Composure. Morning, noon, or evening bath. Balances and refreshes the mind, body and spirit.

Blue - Calm, Peaceful, Relaxing. Mid-day and/or evening bath. Blue is calming for the restless child.

Indigo -Tranquillity, Understanding. Excellent for an evening bath. Excellent for a hyperactive child and insomnia. Tranquil to all of the senses Indigo is ideal for a peaceful sleep and to increase dream activity.

Violet - Creativity, Imagination. Morning, mid-day, and/or evening bath. Violet can stimulate dream time before bedtime or napping and expand the ability to fantasize.

MENTAL EXERCISES

What children see and imagine has a direct and powerful effect on their entire self. What children think, they become through their senses. Children become what they *think* they are. Therefore, it is important for children to think positive and creative thoughts which creates a balanced and beautiful individual. Knowing the proper use of colors will help provide understanding, personal development and greater awareness of their whole self.

IMAGERY

Children can be taught to imagine with color. Before they perform a task select a color that pertains to its achievement. Ask the child to close her/his eyes and imagine the color in her/his mind. Have fun with the color exercises and note the results.

Red - Think **red** to have courage and motivation, especially to start or complete a task at hand. Think rosy pink to rejuvenate the body and mind, especially after an illness or injury. Think pink to send someone love and affection.

Orange - Think **orange** to become more sociable, to increase the appetite, and to perform determined emotionally charged action. It's the winner's color.

90

Yellow - Think yellow for positive energy, to organize thoughts, to memorize information and to make important decisions. Think yellow to be happy.

Green - Think green to balance and to heal the mind, body, and spirit. Green helps increase self-esteem, personal power and the will-power to endure under adverse circumstances. Think green to refresh and regenerate the body and mind!

Blue - Contemplate blue to acquire inner peace, to relax the body, and to soothe the mind. Feel the entire self become emotionally balanced.

Indigo - Visualize indigo to make logical decisions, to handle daily tasks efficiently and to induce a deep, relaxing sleep. Feel its tranquil vibration to become mentally balanced.

Violet - Think violet to exercise good judgment, to make positive choices and to calm the body's nervous system. Think warm magenta to stimulate the creative imagination and dream time before a nap or bedtime.

Brown - Think brown to feel safe and secure and to center children from an emotionally charged day. It can ground them from a frantic and confusing pace.

Gray has a sobering effect upon the mind. Think gray to hold back angry words and emotional outbursts. Gray is the great stablilizer for mental and emotional excessiveness.

White - Think or contemplate on white to forgive someone. White can clear your mind of all negative thoughts. Think white to start a new begining.

MEDITATION

The main objectives of meditation for children are the development of the creative imagination and concentration. Other objectives include greater awareness and the development of different levels of the mind; intuition, self-direction, self-observation, emotional calm, and readiness to learn. For children over age 8 meditation helps develop control and understanding of their desires and emotions. Meditation with color is beneficial for the body, mind, emotions and spirit.

HOW TO LEAD A MEDITATION

1. Have the children sit up with the spine straight or lie down with the entire body in a straight line with arms at their side.

2. It is important to first have the children do several deep breathing exercises. Instruct them to breath in and out of the mouth to a count of 5. Repeat this breathing exercise 5-7 times.

3. Instruct the children to imagine a rainbow in their mind. Have them breath in a rainbow through the mouth and breath out a rainbow through their mouth to a count of 5.

4. Select a color meditation below for a specific goal.

Have fun improvising words and experimenting. For example, choose the color blue before bedtime for the child to have a restful and calm sleep. Tell the child to imagine a blue cloud or beautiful ocean and do the 5 count while the child envisions and breathes. Younger children concentrate for a shorter time spent. Keep it short and sweet. Eventually the children may use color meditation on their own. If a child is anticipating a spelling test the following day use the color yellow, if they have nightmares use the color green. Speak each exercise slowly with a voice that reflects the specific color result. (Red is a more exciting sound than blue) For example speak of yellow with a happy voice, blue with a calm voice and violet with an imaginative voice. Improvise with the following color breathing examples and enjoy!

Red - Close your eyes and visualize the color red as you breathe it into your body through your feet and up through your head. Sit or lie down with your spine straight and imagine the color red as a brilliant red laser beam. In your mind's eye, see the room filled with red and breathe red. Allow the color red to enter your entire body and feel its dynamic energy penetrate every cell of your body. Feel red flowing through your blood stream, saturating your entire body from head to toe with pure energy. Now feel the invigorating force of its vibration and become one with this powerful force. Become thoroughly energized!

Orange - Close your eyes and sit straight. Now imagine yourself in an orange room where everything surrounding you is orange. Take a deep breath of orange and let it fill you with its incandescent glow. Feel the orange atmosphere penetrate your entire body. Continue to take several deep breaths, each time taking in the breath more slowly, until your breathing is gentle and controlled. As you breathe in the orange essence, begin to feel its vital force and become completely awakened with vitality.

Yellow - Visualize the warm, golden rays of the sun beaming upon you, engulfing you, penetrating your skin and illuminating your mind. Breathe in the golden yellow rays as they bring understanding and clarity to your consciousness.

Green - Close your eyes and imagine yourself walking in an emerald green forest surrounding a body of water. Allow the fresh green grass and the clear turquoise water to engulf your entire body. Breathe in the refreshing emerald green and feel its soothing vibrations balance your body, mind, and spirit. Now allow the balancing properties of green to restore, refresh and regenerate your entire being. Feel life pulsating through and around you! Awaken to life!

Blue - Close your eyes and imagine yourself floating on a cloud in the air. Absorb the cool and calming blue sky into yourself. Breathe its peaceful vibrations and allow your skin to absorb its cooling, cleansing, and purifying effects into every cell of your body. Be calm and at peace.

Indigo - Feel an indigo (royal blue) light penetrate gently at the middle of your forehead. Imagine yourself holding the earth in the palm of your hands. Caress the world to your heart. Now sense your universal connection with all the world; feel the unity and oneness of all living creatures. Absorb the vibration of unconditional love. Now you are one with all the earth and the Creator. Feel the love.

Violet - Allow the violet ray to flow through the top of your head, all the way down through the bottom of your feet. Breathe in the color violet and direct it in your mind's eye. Feel its energy expand your awareness, imagination and intuitive self. Now surround yourself with violet light for Divine guidance and a spectacular creative day!

93

White - See yourself surrounded by bright dazzling white lights. Breathe in white light and breathe out white light through every pore of your skin and every part of your body. Imagine yourself in the center of an oval of radiant white light. Feel cleansed; feel free; feel anew!

Gray - Visualize a smoky gray cloud whenever you need to control your temper (substitute a behavior that needs controlled). Allow the cloud to float over your head to control obsessive thoughts; over your mouth to control bitter or negative words; over your chest to prevent anxiety; over your heart to neutralize hate; and over your stomach to avoid over-indulgences. Meditate on gray for self-control and moderation in all excessive things.

Black - Black has no positive use in meditation, because of its negative connotation throughout Western history.

Brown - Visualize yourself standing barefoot on the earth hugging a big brown tree. Breathe in the earth's and the majestic tree's brown energy of strength and stability. Become one with the tree and allow your feet to become the roots of the tree. Feel the heart beat of the earth pulsate through you. Feel grounded, safe, secure and at one with nature and all life!

Metallic - Visualize yourself covered in sparkling golden sequins. Walk directly into the path of the dazzling warm rays of the sun and allow the rays of sunlight to flash off you in all directions. Become like a mirror reflecting the powerful glow of the sun and shine your rays of love and joy as beauty to everyone. Become exhilarated by the *sunsation!*

Iridescent - Visualize yourself sitting in a cosmic rain shower. Observe the falling rain as it sprinkles on your face. Concentrate on one raindrop at a time. See the myriad glistening colors of the rainbow running up and down the raindrop. Become the splendid hues as they change colors to the rhythm of your breathing. Experience what it feels like to become each color; see it and feel it. Become red, orange, yellow, green, blue, indigo and violet in iridescent hues. Now feel what it's like to become a rainbow. Breathe a rainbow into your heart and have a rainbow day!

FUN WITH AURAS

The life force around us is called the aura. The aura is a partially visible electromagnetic field emitted from our physical and spirit body. The aura engulfs our entire body from head to toe. Saints and angels have been depicted with a luminous halo or a cloud-like colorful emanation radiating from their heads and bodies. As an ethereal radiation, the aura projects the vibrations from our essence and indicates the mental, physical, spiritual state and the expression of our unique personality. Most auras of people are one or multi-colored according to the thoughts, health, personality and emotions of the individual. When there are various colors there is a tendency for one color to dominate.

The colors can be iridescent, sparkley, misty, and soft in appearance. Auras can appear to pulsate and glimmer and can extend from two to three feet out from the body in straight lines or unfold like spirals. Others can appear as a halo or cloud above the head or as patches or specks of light surrounding the body. The inner layer extending directly from the body to two to three inches is the health aura. The hazy aura surrounding this layer depicts the personality and state of mind of the individual. The inner aura for both children and adults is similar in size and shape. However, the outer layer of a child extends approximately four inches. An aura can be sensed by odor or heat and under the proper conditions can be seen with the naked eye. Our true character traits can be determined by the colors of our aura, our very own unique magnetic atmosphere.

Young babies from newborns through the age of three can see auras naturally. Very few individuals see auras throughout their life. However, besides the naked eye other tools such as Color Therapy glasses can aid in seeing an aura. The indigo, violet, blue or green Color Therapy glasses are an excellent easy tool for viewing the aura. Even individuals that are blind may not see the aura, but can sense its vibrations. All animals, especially cats and dogs sense the vibration of an aura of a person and respond accordingly. There are a variety of ways to learn how to read an aura. The following methods are simple and successful for everyone. Have fun and for interpretation of the colors refer to the chart entitled "Colors of Auras and Indications" (p. 99).

Simple Techniques For Viewing Your Aura

Anyone can develop the special visual sensitivity that is required to see auras, even your own. Fully extend your right arm above your head, your right palm facing the ceiling. Without blinking your eyes, fix your eyes on the tip of one of your fingers. Do not break your concentration, if you do, begin again. Continue to practice gazing intensely at one fixed spot. Eventually, you will see an emanation of light around your hand, while you gaze at the tip of your finger. It is very common to see the colors white, yellow, or blue at first. With more practice you will possibly begin to see multiple colors and even various forms. If you are wearing indigo, violet, blue or green Color Therapy glasses you just have to glance at your finger tip to see your aura. If you are wearing Color Therapy glasses make certain you have enough light to look effectively through them. You will see the aura, but it will be impossible to see the true colors.

Once you've mastered this technique try to read your aura by standing in front of a mirror, preferably with a white or light and plain background behind you. Wear white or light colored clothing. Begin to focus at the top of your head or the tip of your shoulder. Practice this same technique with others, including animals, plants and inanimate objects (a book is excellent) by placing them against a white or light background. It's that simple!

VIEWING A CHILD'S AURA

Have the child stand against a wall or solid colored back-ground. Place her/his hands with palms of hands against the wall. She/he must remain still the entire time of your viewing. Stand at least 10 feet away. Concentrate your eyes at the tip of the shoulder or the very top of the head. Allow your eyes without blinking to stare at a fixed point. You will begin to see a white glowing haze outline the body. With your eyes gazing in the same position and without blinking, ask the child to move completely away from the wall and out of your sight. As you stare at the wall you will see an after image of the entire body. Practice this technique and experience a "WOW, I can see it!"

HEAD TO TOE TECHNIQUE

This is one of the simplest methods for viewing an aura. You will be amazed at what you will see. Place the child in a standing position with the legs spread out about a foot apart. Allow the arms to be extended straight across with the palm of the hands facing and touching the wall. You need to stand at least 10 feet away from the child. Stare at any outer point of body; the tip of a finger, the top of the head or the edge of a shoulder works best. Stare without your eyes blinking for as long as you can, at least one minute. As you keep your eyes focused on the same spot instruct the child to move completely away from the wall while you keep your eyes on the same spot. You will see the emanation of the aura as an outline of the entire body. Keep practicing to see colors and more detailed forms. Consider keeping a record of the colors of the aura an the shape for each day or whenever you read the aura. The mood and/or physical condition of the child can change the colors of the aura.. Have fun exploring.

ARM AND HAND TECHNIQUE

Place the child in a standing or sitting position sideways against the wall. Have the subject straighten out her/his arm with the palm of the hand flat against the wall. Stand at least 10 feet away and stare at the tip of her/his middle finger for as long as you can without blinking. Keep your eyes focused on the same spot as you instruct the child to lower her/his arm. As you continue to stare at the same spot you will see her/his aura.

Throughout your experimentation with reading auras keep a calendar of the day and time with the precise colors and forms that you see with every aura viewing. Before bedtime, upon awakening, when the child is cranky or any particular time of day or special situation view the child's aura and note the changes in color and forms. Refer to the chart on page 99 for the meaning of the colors of auras. Now try viewing the aura of a plant or your pet. You can also teach children how to view your aura and their pet's aura.

The shapes of the aura hold special meaning, especially for children's auras. The following chart provides interpretations for the shapes of children's auras.

97

INTERPRETATIONS OF SHAPES OF A CHILD'S AURA

A child that accepts instruction, is sensible and has the ability to concentrate will have a crown shaped aura around the head.

A child that needs more guidance and learns best by examples will have a multitude of colors with sharp shapes and points that create a full figure aura.

A child that is uncontrollable and hyperactive will have an aura that is chain like around the shoulders and/or a very weak emanation around the head.

CONCLUSION

The experiments and various techniques in this chapter are intended for fun. Enjoy exploring a rainbow world of auras. Have a *Rainbow Day*!

The author welcomes your comments and your experience with **Color Therapy For Children.** You can contact Ms. Hoffman at her:

E-mail address: Maryanne @ RAINBOWRISING.COM.

Web site: WWW.RAINBOWRISING.COM.

Web site: WWW.STARVISIONS.COM.

Write Maryanne at:
Rainbow Rising Institute of American Color Therapy
P.O. Box 93
Hartstown, PA. 16131

COLORS OF AURAS AND INDICATIONS

Pink - love, affectionate, refinement, aesthetic, modest
Salmon Pink - Universal Love, comfort, joy
Deep Pink - loving nature
Rose Red - deep love of family, patriotic
Red - strong desire, defiant, red flashes - anger
Bright Red- courage, hope, vitality
Dark Red - ambition, vitality
Muddy or Cloudy Red - temper, restless, hyperactivity
Orange Red - physically healing, revitalizing
Orange - ambition, pride, thoughtfulness, consideration
Yellow Orange - self-control, wise beyond years, spiritual
Brownish Orange - repression, laziness
Yellow - intellectual, positive disposition, optimistic
Lemon Yellow - artistic, mental agility, inventive
Golden Yellow - balanced mind and healthy body
Yellow with Red - inferiority complex, shy
Green - benevolence, abundance, peace, healing, focused
Emerald Green - versatility, healing ability, trustworthy
Aqua - high ideals, peace, healing love
Light Delicate Green - compassion, sympathy
Grayish Yellow Green - shrewd, deceit, untruthful
Blue- Violet - accomplishments through inspiration
Red-Violet - strong will, physical power
Blue - healing love, spiritual understanding, inspiration, calm
Light Blue - devotion to ideals, spiritual learning
Deep Blue - loyalty, honesty, unselfish dedication
Indigo - Violet - spiritual seeker, creative
Indigo - excellent judgment, realistic, love for everyone
Lavender (pale purple) - humility, imaginative
Orchid (tinge of pink) - spiritual, special, pure, ingenuity
Purple - spiritually practical, true greatness, unselfish efforts
Brownish Red - over-indulgent, lazy
Brown - industrious, orderly, effort, perseverance
Grayish Brown - selfishness, unpleasant
Greenish Brown - jealousy, mean
Gray - fear, sorrow, grief
Silver - individualistic
Black Patches - hatred and malice
Black with Red - vicious, ruthless
Pearl White (opalescent) - gentleness, kindness, forgiving
Crystal White - spiritual self-mastery
Iridescent hues - highly spiritual, gifted and talented.

Bibliography

An extensive amount of research has been conducted through workshops and teaching experiences of a wide and varied population over the past fifteen years. This field experience coupled with information from my book, *THE RAINBOW IN YOUR LIFE,* comprises the majority of the contents. The references listed below have been valuable resources that have guided and substantiated portions of this book.

Birren, Faber: *Color Psychology and Color Therapy*, The Citadel Press, Secaucus, N. J., 1961.

Clark, Linda: *The Ancient Art of Color Therapy*, Pocket Books, New York, N.Y.

Davidoff, Jules B.: *Cognition Through Color*, MIT Press, Cambridge, Mass.,1991.

Dennis, Caryl: *Colorology*, Rainbow Unlimited, Clearwater, Fl.,1990.

Hoffman, Maryanne E.: *The Goddess Guide*, Star Visions, Solon, Oh., 1990.

Hoffman, Maryanne E.: *The Rainbow In Your Life*, Star Visions, Solon, Oh., 1993.

Luscher, Max, Ph. D.: *The Luscher Color Test*, Pocket Books, New York, N.Y.

Luscher, Max, Ph. D.: *The 4-Color Person*, Pocket Books, New York, N.Y. 1980.

Regush, Nicholas, M.: *The Human Aura*, Berkley Publishing Corporation, New Yofk, N. Y., 1974.

Rozman, Deborah: *Meditating with Children*, University of the Trees Press, Boulder Creek, CA., 1977.

Mystical Messages ™

Visionary Greeting Cards
by MARYANNE E. HOFFMAN

Vivid   Sunsation   Colorful   Unique Paintings

These exquisite cards are six color lithographed with metallic gold on high quality recycled paper and suitable for framing. The vivid colors and whimsical images are fun for children of all ages. Keepsakes for years to come!

ALL OCCASION FANTASY - a variety of 12 different inspiring, festive, celestial and vibrant magical images. Front cover included.

PERSONAL ZODIAC BIRTHDAY - Each zodiac card gives a unique message describing the sun sign, including fortunate days and lucky numbers. Available blank or versed. Please specify.

$2.50 each SPECIAL OFFER $25.00 a set/ DOZEN! Save $5!

✦✦

SPECTRUM ART PRINTS - LIMITED EDITION OF 250
By MARYANNE E. HOFFMAN

A collectable, numbered and hand-signed original print 22"X22"- the Spectrum art at the beginning of each chapter of **COLOR THERAPY for CHILDREN**. Experience these beautiful absorbing healing colors for the child's favorite room.

Available: Red Spectrum (p. 12). Yellow Spectrum - with metallic gold (p. 23), Green Spectrum (p. 54) and Blue Spectrum (p. 60).

✦✦

INQUIRIES about Maryanne's workshops and services and to place an order for her special products 1-877-4STAR33 Master Card/Visa.

FREE Greeting Card (art on the front cover) when you order Maryanne's color catalog of her products and services. Send $3.00 (refundable with your firsts order).

☆ Star Visions Order Dept. ☆
P.O. Box 39683
Solon, Ohio 44139
Email: Maryanne@STARVISIONS.COM US
Web Site WWW.STARVISIONS.COM US

BY *Maryanne Hoffman*

VIDEOS

The Rainbow In Your Life
A personal journey through the visual color meditations with an introduction to all the colors and their specific meaning. You will be color tested and learn how to read auras.

Color Therapy I
Color in everyday life with various special techniques on individual color testing and color applications. Hands-on instructional material that is required toward Color Therapy certification.

Color Therapy II
Hands-on Color Therapy techniques with special emphasis on color applications, integrated color testing. A continuation of Color Therapy I. Instructional material that is required toward Color Therapy certification.

Color Specialties
How to get the affect you want using color. A variety of color applications and important power colors for the individual and professions of all types. Simple Color testing included.

CASSETTES

The Rainbow In Your Life
Maryanne's soothing voice guides through the spectrum of your rainbow, as it applies to all the aspects of your life. For relaxation, motivation and health. Includes color health chart. 60 min. $12.95.

Visual Spectrum Meditations
Maryanne leads you through the images and essence of each spectrum illustrations from her book *The Rainbow In Your Life*. A richly fulfilling journey awaits you. $9.95. Cassette with book or with a set of 8 vivid **Color Cards** 51/2" X 7". $21.95.

The Astro*Guide Yearly Forecast
Maryanne's month to month predictions for your birth sign for the entire year. Detailed and specific forecast for money, love, career, family, travel, health, etc. $19.95. In booklet form $7.95.

Rainbow Rising
Institute of American Color Therapy
Invites you to become a Charter Member of the

AMERICAN COLOR THERAPY ASSOCIATION

Anyone can join! Receive special gifts and discounts!

Maryanne Hoffman founded the AMERICAN COLOR THERAPY ASSOCIATION for you to benefit from the knowledge of the rainbow in your life. As a charter member you will receive a set of full color note cards (6) of the rainbow illustrated by Ms. Hoffman, Rainbow Rising Color Therapy magazine and discounts on workshops, seminars and color therapy products. Charter membership is $35.00 for one year. Join today and be informed of the new developments in the field of color therapy. We honor master card/Visa.

◆◆◆

COLOR THERAPY PRODUCTS
For MIND, BODY AND SPIRIT

✦ **Rainbow Bath-** selection of seven vibrant colors of the spectrum for a color bath experience. Color is energy and water conducts energy. A rainbow bath will energize your child.

✦ **Color Therapy Glasses** - selection of seven different colors of the rainbow (precise vibration of the spectrum). Each color has a specific benefit. As light enters the eyes it becomes the color ray of the specific color glasses.

✦ **Color Covers (acetate overlays)-** a rainbow selection plus pink for reading, learning and behavior modification.

RAINBOW RISING
INSTITUTE OF
AMERICAN COLOR THERAPY
&
American Color Therapy Association
P.O. Box 93
Hartstown, PA. 16131
**FAX (724) 932-5944 Ph.(724)932-5019
WWW.RAINBOWRISING.COM** US
Email: Maryanne @RAINBOWRISING.COM
US